ESB X

Parent/Teacher Edition

6

Show What You K[illegible] the COMMON CORE

D1397822

Assessing Student Knowledge of the Common Core State Standards (CCSS)

Reading

823

Published by:

Show What You Know® Publishing
A Division of Englefield & Associates, Inc.
P.O. Box 341348
Columbus, OH 43234-1348
Phone: 614-764-1211
www.showwhatyouknowpublishing.com

Copyright © 2011 by Englefield & Associates, Inc.

All rights reserved. No part of this book, including interior design, cover design, and icons, may be reproduced or transmitted in any form, by any means (electronic, photocopying, recording, or otherwise). Permission to reproduce the Correlation Charts on pages 45, 46, 69, and 70 is granted by the publisher to one teacher for use in a single classroom.

Standards are from the Common Core State Standards Initiative Web site at www.corestandards.org dated 2011.

Printed in the United States of America
13 12 11 20 19 18 17 16 15 14 13 12 11 10 9 8 7 6 5 4 3 2 1

ISBN: 1-59230-457-5

Limit of Liability/Disclaimer of Warranty: The authors and publishers have used their best efforts in preparing this book. Englefield & Associates, Inc., and the authors make no representations or warranties with respect to the contents of this book and specifically disclaim any implied warranties and shall in no event be liable for any loss of any kind including but not limited to special, incidental, consequential, or other damages.

Acknowledgements

Show What You Know® Publishing acknowledges the following for their efforts in making this assessment material available for students, parents, and teachers:

Cindi Englefield, President/Publisher
Eloise Boehm-Sasala, Vice President/Managing Editor
Jennifer Harney, Editor/Illustrator

About the Contributors

The content of this book was written BY teachers FOR teachers and students and was designed specifically for the Common Core State Standards for Grade 6 Reading. Contributions to the Reading section of this book were also made by the educational publishing staff at Show What You Know® Publishing. Dr. Jolie S. Brams, a clinical child and family psychologist, is the contributing author of the Test Anxiety and Test-Taking Strategies chapters of this book. Without the contributions of these people, this book would not be possible.

LEROY COLLINS LEON COUNTY
PUBLIC LIBRARY SYSTEM
200 West Park Avenue
Tallahassee, Florida 32301-7720

J 372.4 SHO Grade 6 Teacher
ed. <cjg>

1634-0245 2/9/2012 ESB

Show what you know on the

Table of Contents

Introduction.......... v

Test Anxiety.......... 1

Test-Taking Strategies.......... 7

Reading.......... 15

- Introduction.......... 15
- Reading Standards.......... 16
- Glossary of Reading Terms.......... 18
- Reading Assessment One.......... 21
  - Answer Key.......... 39
  - Skills Chart.......... 43
  - Correlation Chart.......... 45
- Reading Assessment Two.......... 47
  - Answer Key.......... 63
  - Skills Chart.......... 67
  - Correlation Chart.......... 69
- Reading Rubrics.......... 71

Copying is Prohibited © Englefield & Associates, Inc.

Introduction

Under the leadership of the National Governors Association (NGA) and the Council of Chief State School Officers (CCSSO), forty-eight states, two territories, and the District of Columbia joined the Common Core State Standards Initiative (CCSSI) in 2009.

The CCSSI has produced Common Core State Standards to provide uniformity and high standards for student achievement in grades K–12 across the nation. These core standards provide a consistent, clear understanding of what students are expected to learn, so teachers and parents have a roadmap for what they need to do to help them. Further, these standards provide appropriate benchmarks for all students, regardless of where they live, and allow states to more effectively help all students to succeed.

To develop these standards, CCSSO and the NGA worked with representatives from participating states, a wide range of educators, content experts, researchers, national organizations, and community groups. The adopted core standards reflect the invaluable feedback from the general public, teachers, parents, business leaders, states, and content area experts.

As reflected in our *Show What You Know® on the Common Core* Student Workbooks and Parent/Teacher Editions for grades 3–8, Reading and Mathematics are the first subjects chosen for the Common Core State Standards because these two subjects are skills, upon which students build skill sets in other subject areas. They are also the subjects most frequently assessed for accountability purposes.

The *Show What You Know® on the Common Core* series for grades 3–8 is designed to review the new core standards and identify areas of students' strengths and needed improvement through diagnostic tests aligned to the core standards. In addition, the series provides chapters on test anxiety, test-taking strategies, and glossaries of terms for Reading and Mathematics to help prepare students with the knowledge and skills they need to succeed in the future.

Common Core State Standards will help ensure that students are receiving a high-quality education consistently, from school to school and state to state. These standards are a first step—a key building block—in providing students with a high-quality education that will prepare them for success in college and careers.

About the Show What You Know® Program

Show What You Know® Publishing has been developing test-preparation products since 1993. These products teach test-taking skills that are specific to state assessments and provide students with practice on full-length tests that simulate the format of state assessments. We understand that many students are not good test takers because they get nervous and may experience test anxiety. To help students with this issue, we provide a chapter, written by a child psychologist, that explains what test anxiety is, what it feels like, and ways to reduce the anxiety before, during, and after testing. Research has proven that three elements must exist for test success: knowledge, test-taking skills, and confidence. The Show What You Know® test-preparation program helps to ensure test success.

How to Use This Program

There are numerous ways to use the Student Workbook and Parent/Teacher Edition to help prepare your students for the Reading assessment. But before your students begin the assessments, take time to review the Test Anxiety and Test-Taking Strategies chapters in the Student Workbook to help them learn how to be better test takers. These important concepts can really improve students' test scores—it works!

Tips to Reduce Test Anxiety

You can read the entire chapter on test anxiety in the Student Workbook, or you can break it up into different sections, allowing yourself plenty of time to discuss and practice the methods suggested to reduce test stress. Identify what test anxiety is, and help students learn the symptoms. Explain to them that test anxiety is normal, and that there are ways it can be overcome. Tell them how being a little nervous will motivate them to do their best, but being very nervous could make them forget information they need to know for the test.

The rest of the Test Anxiety chapter offers activities to show ways to overcome test stress, such as thinking positively instead of negatively, emphasizing the importance of good physical health, and studying and practicing for the test. These are skills that will help your students succeed on state assessments, as well as other tests your students will face throughout their lives.

Test-Taking Strategies That Work!

The Test-Taking Strategies chapter can be used in a class discussion. The chapter gives specific test-taking strategies for state assessments. After reviewing the chapter, ask students if they have found ways to help them prepare for tests. Maybe they like to read stories with their parents or they make sure to get extra sleep the week of a test. All of these strategies can be used to help them do well on state assessments and other tests.

Copying is Prohibited © Englefield & Associates, Inc.

The Purpose of the Assessments

After you have walked your students through the Test Anxiety and Test-Taking Strategies chapters, students can take two, 40-question assessments for Reading.

These tests were designed to simulate state assessments so that students can become familiar with the actual look of the test. The more familiar students are with the look of the test, the more confidence they will have when they take the actual assessment.

Correlation Charts Track Students' Strengths and Weaknesses

In this Parent/Teacher Edition, there are Correlation Charts for each Assessment. The standards as well as test item answers are listed for each question. To use the chart, write the students' names in the left-hand column. When students miss a question, place an "X" in the corresponding box. A column with a large number of "Xs" shows that your class needs more practice with that particular standard. You can quickly identify the needs of individual students.

Answer Key with Sample Responses

Answers to the Reading assessments are provided in the Parent/Teacher Edition. The correct answer is given, and for short-answer questions, a sample response is offered.

Skills Chart

A skills chart for each assessment is provided in the Parent/Teacher Edition. The chart serves as a mini directory identifying the Common Core State Standard used for each assessment question, the correct answer choice, and the keyword(s) which summarize(s) the standard.

Additional Teaching Tools

A glossary of Reading terms is provided in the Student Workbook to help your students understand terms that they should be familiar with in the sixth grade.

Suggested Timeline for Program Use

Now that you have a better understanding of how to use the Show What You Know® Test-Preparation Program, here is a suggested timeline for you to use to incorporate the program into your teaching schedule:

Suggested Timeline for Using the Show What You Know® on the Common Core for Grade 6 Reading, Student Workbook	
Week 1	Test Anxiety chapter
Week 2	Test-Taking Strategies chapter
Week 3	Review Glossary of Terms for Reading
Week 4	Reading Assessment One
Week 5	Additional Review After Results of Reading Assessment One
Week 6	Reading Assessment Two

Thank you for implementing the Show What You Know® Test-Preparation Program in your classroom. Good luck to you and all of your students as they prepare for their state assessments!

 Copying is Prohibited © Englefield & Associates, Inc.

Test Anxiety

Introduction

The contents of the Test Anxiety chapter, from the *Show What You Know® on the Common Core for Grade 6 Reading, Student Workbook*, begin on the next page. This chapter will help students begin to understand why they may feel some anxiety before taking a test. This anxiety is normal and is experienced by many people, not only students. The chapter offers information on different types of test takers and ideas on how to reduce worrisome feelings about tests.

Test Anxiety

What is Test Anxiety?

Test anxiety is just a fancy name for feeling nervous about tests. Everyone knows what it is like to be nervous. Feeling nervous is not a good experience.

Many students have anxiety about taking tests, so if you are a test worrier, don't let it worry you. Most likely, many of your fellow students and friends also have fearful feelings about tests but do not share these feelings with others. Sixth grade is a time when everyone wants to seem "grown up," and few sixth graders want to look weak or afraid in the eyes of their friends or their teachers. But not talking to others about anxiety only makes the situation worse. It makes you feel alone and also makes you wonder if there is something "wrong" with you. Be brave! Talk to your friends and teachers about test anxiety. You will feel better for sharing.

What Does It Feel Like to Have Test Anxiety?

Students who have test anxiety don't always feel the same way, but they always feel bad. Here are some ways that students feel when they are anxious about tests.

- **Students who have test anxiety rarely think good things about themselves.**
  They lack confidence in their abilities, and they are convinced they will do poorly on tests. Not only do they feel bad about themselves and their abilities, but they just can't keep negative thoughts out of their minds. They would probably make terrible detectives, because in spite of all the good things they could find out about themselves, they only think about what they can't do. And that's not the worst of it. Students with test anxiety also exaggerate. When they think of the smallest problem, it becomes a hundred times bigger, especially when they think about tests. They are very unforgiving of themselves. If they make a mistake, they always think the worst or exaggerate the situation. If they do poorly on a quiz, they never say, "Well, it's just a quiz, and I'll try better next time." Instead they think, "That test was terrible and I can only imagine how badly I'll do next week." For students with test anxiety, there is never a brighter day ahead. They don't think many good thoughts about themselves, and they certainly don't have a happy outlook on their lives.

- **Students who have test anxiety have poor "thinking habits."**
  Negative thinking is a habit just like any other habit. Some habits are good and some habits are bad, but negative thinking is probably the worst habit of all. A habit forms when you do something over and over again until it becomes so much a part of you that you don't think about it anymore. Students with test anxiety get into bad thinking habits. They develop negative ways of thinking about themselves and about schoolwork, especially about tests. They tend to make the worst out of situations and imagine all kinds of possibilities that probably will not happen. Their thoughts grow like a mushroom out of control. Besides having negative ideas about tests, they begin to have negative ideas about almost everything else in their lives. This is not a good way of thinking because the more negative they feel about themselves, the worse they do in school, and bad grades make them feel even worse about themselves. What a mess. Students who have constant negative thoughts about themselves and schoolwork probably have test anxiety.

- **Students who have test anxiety may feel physically uncomfortable or even ill.**
  It is important to know that your mind and body are connected. What goes on in your mind can change how your body feels, and how your body feels can influence what goes on in your thinking. When students have test anxiety, their thoughts might cause them to have physical symptoms which include a fast heartbeat, butterflies in the stomach, headaches, and all sorts of other physical problems. Some kids become so ill they end up going to the doctor because they believe they are truly sick. Some students miss a lot of school due to anxiety, but they aren't really ill. Instead, their thoughts are controlling their bodies in a negative way. Some anxious students do not realize that what they are feeling is anxiety. They miss many days of school, not because they are lazy or neglectful, but because they believe they truly are not feeling well. Unfortunately, the more school they miss, the more behind they are and the more nervous they feel. Students who suffer from test anxiety probably feel even worse on test days. Their uncomfortable physical feelings will make them either avoid the test completely or feel so bad during the test that they do poorly. Guess what happens then. They feel even worse about themselves, become more anxious, and the cycle goes on and on.

- **Students who have test anxiety "freak out" and want to escape.**
  Many students feel so bad when they are anxious that they will do anything to avoid that feeling. For most students, this means running away from problems, especially tests. Some students try to get away from tests by missing school. This does not solve any problems; the more a student is away from school, the harder schoolwork is, and the worse he or she feels. Some students worry about being worried. It may sound silly, but they are worried that they are going to freak out, and guess what happens . . . they do. They are so terrified that they will have uncontrollable anxious feelings that they actually get anxious feelings when thinking about this problem. For many students, anxiety is such a bad feeling that they will do anything not to feel anxious, even if it means failing tests or school. Although they know this will cause them problems in the future, their anxiety is so overwhelming they would rather avoid anxiety now and fail later. Unfortunately, this is usually what happens.

- **Students who have test anxiety do not show what they know on tests.**
  Students who have test anxiety do not make good decisions on tests. Instead of focusing their thoughts, planning out their answers, and using what they know, students find themselves "blanking out." They stare at the paper, and no answer is there. They become "stuck" and cannot move on. Some students come up with the wrong answers because their anxiety gets in the way of reading directions carefully and thinking about answers thoughtfully. Their minds are running in a hundred different ways and none of those ways seem to be getting them anywhere. They forget to use what they know, and they also forget to use study skills that can help students do their best. When students are so worried that they cannot make good decisions and use all of the talents they have, it is called test anxiety.

Are You One of These "Test-Anxious" Sixth Graders?

As you have seen, students with test anxiety have negative thoughts about themselves, often feel anxious to the point of being ill, freak out and want to escape, and rarely show what they know on tests. Do any of the following kids remind you of yourself?

Stay-Away Stephanie
Stephanie's thoughts tell her it is better to stay away from challenges, especially tests. Stephanie is a good girl, but she is always in trouble at school for avoiding tests. Sometimes, she really feels ill and begs her mom to allow her to stay home on test days. At other times, Stephanie does anything to avoid school, refusing to get up in the morning or to leave the house to catch the bus. Stephanie truly believes there is nothing worse than taking a test. She is so overwhelmed with anxiety that she forgets about the problems that will happen when she stays away from her responsibilities. Unfortunately, the more she stays away, the worse the situation becomes. Stay-Away Stephanie feels less nervous when she doesn't face a test, but she never learns to face her fears.

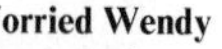

Worried Wendy
Wendy is the type of sixth grader who always expects the worst thing to happen. She has many negative thoughts. Even when situations have turned out to be OK, Wendy focuses on the few bad things that happened. She exaggerates negative events and forgets about everything good. Her mind races a mile a minute with all sorts of thoughts and ideas about tests. The more she thinks, the worse she feels, and her problems become unbelievably huge. Instead of just worrying about a couple of difficult questions on a test, she finds herself thinking about failing the whole test, being made fun of by her friends, being grounded by her parents, and never going to college. She completely forgets that her parents would never be so strict, that her friends like her for many more reasons than her test grades, and that she has all sorts of career choices ahead of her. No one is going to hold it against her if she performed poorly on a test. It is not going to ruin her life. However, Wendy believes all of that would happen. Her negative thoughts get in the way of thinking anything positive.

Critical Chris

Chris is the type of sixth grader who spends all of his time putting himself down. No matter what happens, he always feels he has been a failure. While some people hold grudges against others, Chris holds grudges against himself. No matter what little mistakes he makes, he can never forget them. Chris has had many good things happen to him in his life, and he has been successful many times. Unfortunately, Chris forgets all the good and only remembers the bad. Because he doesn't appreciate himself, Chris has test anxiety.

Victim Vince

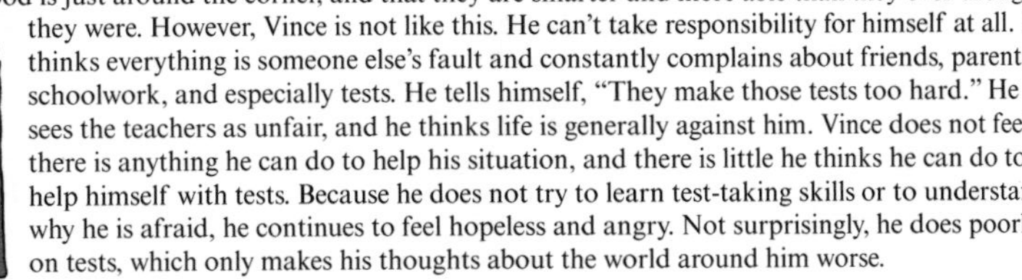

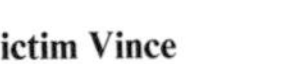

Most sixth graders find it is important to take responsibility for their actions. It helps them understand that adulthood is just around the corner, and that they are smarter and more able than they ever thought they were. However, Vince is not like this. He can't take responsibility for himself at all. He thinks everything is someone else's fault and constantly complains about friends, parents, schoolwork, and especially tests. He tells himself, "They make those tests too hard." He sees the teachers as unfair, and he thinks life is generally against him. Vince does not feel there is anything he can do to help his situation, and there is little he thinks he can do to help himself with tests. Because he does not try to learn test-taking skills or to understand why he is afraid, he continues to feel hopeless and angry. Not surprisingly, he does poorly on tests, which only makes his thoughts about the world around him worse.

Perfect Pat

Everyone knows that there is more homework and responsibility in sixth grade than in previous grades. Everyone in the sixth grade needs to try his or her best, but no one should try as much as Pat does. All Pat does is worry. No matter what she does, it's never good enough. She will write book reports over and over and study for tests until she is exhausted. Trying hard is fine, but no matter what Pat does, she feels she has never done enough. Because she never accomplishes what she sets out to do (that would be impossible), she worries all the time. Her anxiety level gets higher and higher. The more anxious she becomes, the worse she does on tests. This just makes her study and worry more. What a terrible situation!

How Do I Handle Test Anxiety?

Test anxiety is a very powerful feeling that convinces students they are weak and helpless. Feelings of test anxiety can be so powerful it seems there is nothing you can do to stop them. Anxiety seems to take over your mind and body and leaves you feeling like you are going to lose the test anxiety battle for sure.

The good news is that there are many simple things you can do to win the battle over test anxiety. If you can learn these skills in the sixth grade, you are on the road to success in school and for all other challenges in your life.

- **Change the way you think.**
  Most of us don't "think about how we think." We just go along thinking our thoughts and never really considering whether they are helpful or not helpful or if they are right or wrong. We rarely realize how much the way we think has to do with how well we get along in life. Our thoughts can influence how we feel about ourselves, how we get along with other people, how well we do in school, and how we perform on tests.
- **The Soda Pop Test.**
  Most sixth graders have heard a parent or teacher tell them, "There is more than one side to any story." One student reported that his grandfather used to say, "There's more than one way to paint a fence." Have you ever considered how you think about different situations? Most situations can be looked at in many ways, both good and bad.

  Take a can of soda pop and put it on your desk or dresser at home. Get out a piece of paper and a pen or a pencil. Now, draw a line down the middle of the paper. On one side, put a heading: "All the bad things about this can of soda pop." On the other side put another heading: "All the good things about this can of soda pop." If you think about that can of soda pop, you might come up with the following chart.

All the bad things about this can of soda pop	All the good things about this can of soda pop
Not an attractive color	Easy-to-read lettering
It's getting warm	Nice to have something to drink
Not much in the can	Inexpensive
Has a lot of sugar	Recyclable aluminum cans

Look how easy it is to write down good things or bad things about a silly can of soda pop. That can of soda pop is not really good or bad, it's just a can of soda pop, but we can either look at it in a positive way or we can think about everything negative that comes to our minds. Doesn't the same thing hold true for tests? Tests are not good or bad in themselves. Tests are just a way to challenge us and see what we know. Challenges can be stressful, but they can also be rewarding. Studying for tests can be boring and can take up a lot of free time, but we can also learn a lot and feel great about ourselves when we study. The way you think about tests will help determine how you do in a test-taking situation. Most importantly, how you feel about tests is related to your level of anxiety about test taking. Students who have negative thoughts and feelings about tests become anxious. Students who think positively are less anxious. To reduce test anxiety, try thinking about tests and testing situations using a positive frame of mind.

- **All or Nothing Thinking.**
  Nothing is ever as simple as it seems. Sometimes we convince ourselves something is going to be "awful" or "wonderful." Rarely does it turn out that way.

  Trouble comes along when students think tests are going to be an "awful" experience. If you dread something happening, it is only going to make things worse. Also, you may be wrong. Nothing is as terrible as it seems. All the negative thoughts you have about the upcoming test cannot possibly be true. Thinking something is "awful" or "terrible" and nothing else only leads to trouble and failure. The more negative you feel about something, the worse things turn out.

  Very few things are "all good" or "all bad." This is especially true for tests. Recognizing the "bad" parts of tests can help you be successful. For example, the fact that you need to study for tests, to pay attention while you are taking tests, and to understand there are probably many more fun things to do in school than take tests are all "true" thoughts. "Good" thoughts are just as true, including the good feelings one gets from studying and the chance that you might do well. Having "all or nothing" thinking is going to get you nowhere. Successful and happy students know some experiences are better than others, but they try to look at a situation from all sides.

- **Mind Reading.**
  Some students believe they can read the minds of their parents and teachers. They assume if they do poorly on a test, everyone will think they are "dumb" or "lazy." The more their minds create all the terrible things that people may say about them, the more anxious they get. This just increases anxiety and definitely does not help students do well on tests.

- **Catastrophizing.**
  When people catastrophize, they make everything a catastrophe. A catastrophe is a disaster. It is when something terrible happens. When a student catastrophizes, his or her mind goes on and on creating terrible scenes of disasters. If someone put all these ideas into a movie script, the writer might be rich.

  Your state proficiency test is an important part of a sixth-grader's school year. It is a test that helps the student, the teacher, and the school. However, a sixth-grade student is much more than just his or her score on the test. Each student is an individual who has his or her own great personality, talents, and other successes in school. If what people catastrophized about was really true, the whole world would be a terrible mess. Imagine if your mother cooked a dinner that didn't turn out quite right. This might mean everyone has to go out for fast food, but you wouldn't love your mother any less. It would be catastrophizing if your mother said, "Now that I burned the dinner, none of my kids will love me. They will probably just want to move out as quickly as they can, and my life will be ruined." Catastrophizing about a test is just as bad. Thinking that this test is going to be the worst experience of your life and that your future will be ruined will not help you feel comfortable when preparing for and taking the test.

- **Making "Should" Statements.**
  Students make themselves anxious when they think they "should" do everything. They feel they "should" be as smart as everyone else, "should" study more, and "should" not feel anxious about tests. All these thoughts are pretty ridiculous. You can't always be as smart as the next person, and you do not have to study until you drop to do well on tests. Instead of kicking yourself for not being perfect, it is better to think about all the good things you have done in your life. This will help you do better on tests and be happier in your life by reducing your anxiety.

How Do I Replace Worried Thoughts with Positive Ones?

As we have learned, there are all kinds of thoughts that make us anxious, such as feeling we "should" do everything, thinking we can read peoples' minds, catastrophizing, and thinking only bad thoughts about a situation. Learning how to stop these types of thoughts is very important. Understanding your thoughts and doing something about them help control test anxiety.

People who are worried or anxious can become happier when thinking positive thoughts. Even when situations are scary, such as a visit to the dentist, "positive imagery" is helpful. "Positive imagery" means thinking good thoughts to keep from thinking anxious thoughts. Positive and negative thoughts do not go together. If you are thinking something positive, it is almost impossible to think of something negative. Keep this in mind when test anxiety starts to become a bother.

Try these ideas the next time you find yourself becoming anxious.

- **Thoughts of Success.**
  Thinking "I can do it" thoughts can chase away thoughts of failure. Imagine times you were successful, such as when you performed well in a dance recital or figured out a complicated brain teaser. These are good things to think about. Telling yourself you have been successful in the past and can be successful in the future will chase away thoughts of anxiety.

- **Relaxing Thoughts.**
  Some people find that thinking calming or relaxing thoughts is helpful. Picturing a time in which you felt comfortable and happy can lessen your anxious feelings. Imagine yourself playing a baseball game, running through a park, or eating an ice cream cone; these are all positive thoughts that may get in the way of anxious ones. Some students find that listening to music on the morning of a test is helpful. It probably doesn't matter what music you listen to, as long as it makes you feel good about yourself, confident, and relaxed.

  Just as you can calm your mind, it is also important for you to relax your body. Practice relaxing your body. When students have test anxiety, their muscles become stiff. In fact, the whole body becomes tense. Taking deep breaths before a test and letting them out slowly as well as relaxing muscles in your body are all very helpful ways to feel less anxious. Your school counselors will probably have more ideas about relaxation. You may find that relaxation doesn't just help you on tests, but is helpful for other challenging situations and for feeling healthy overall.

- **Don't Let Yourself Feel Alone.**
  Everyone feels more anxious when they feel alone and separate from others. Talking to your friends, parents, and teachers about your feelings helps. Feeling anxious about tests does not mean there is something wrong with you. You will be surprised to find that many of your friends and fellow students also feel anxious about tests. You may be even more surprised to learn your parents and teachers have also had test anxiety. They know what you are going through and are there to support you.

- **Take Care of Yourself.**
  Everyone is busy. Many sixth graders are involved in all sorts of activities, including sports, music, and helping around the house. Often, you are so busy you forget to eat breakfast or you don't get enough sleep. Eating and sleeping right are important, especially before a test like your state proficiency test. If you are not a big breakfast eater, try to find something that you like to eat and get in the habit of eating breakfast. When you do not eat right, you may feel shaky and have a hard time concentrating, and your anxiety can increase. Being tired does not help either. Try to get in the habit of going to bed at a good time every night (especially the night before a test) so you can feel fresh, rested, and confident.

- **Practice Your Test-Taking Success.**
  People who have accomplished incredibly difficult goals have used their imaginations to help them achieve success. They thought about what they would do step by step to be successful.

  You can do the same. Think about yourself on the morning of the test. Imagine telling yourself positive thoughts and eating a good breakfast. Think about arriving at school and feeling confident that you will do fine on the test. Imagine closing your eyes before the test, breathing deeply, relaxing, and remembering all the study skills you have learned. The more you program your mind to think in a successful and positive way, the better off you will be.

- **Learn to Use Study Skills.**
  The next chapter in this book will help you learn test-taking strategies. The more you know about taking tests successfully, the calmer you will feel. Knowledge is power. Practice test-taking strategies to reduce your test anxiety.

- **Congratulate Yourself During the Test.**
  Instead of thinking, "I've only done five problems and I've got eight pages to go," or "I knew three answers were right but one mixed me up," reward yourself for what you have done. Tell yourself, "I got some answers right so far, so I bet I can do more." After all, if you don't compliment yourself, who will?

Conclusion

You are not alone if you feel stressed about tests. It is probably good to feel a little anxious, because it motivates you to do well. However, if you feel very anxious about tests, then reading, re-reading, and practicing the suggestions in this chapter will help you "tackle your test anxiety."

Test-Taking Strategies

Introduction

The contents of the Test-Taking Strategies chapter from the S*how What You Know® on the Common Core for Grade 6 Reading, Student Workbook*, begin on the next page. This chapter will introduce students to test-taking strategies. These strategies are hints students can use for any test, but they are especially helpful for state assessments. This chapter will give students the tools they need to become successful test takers.

Test-Taking Strategies

All Students Can Do Their Best on Tests!

Most students want to do their best on tests. Tests are one important way for teachers to know how well students are doing and for students to understand how much progress they are making in their studies. Tests, like your state proficiency test, help schools measure how well students are learning so teachers and principals can make their schools even better. Students can do the best job possible in "showing what they know" by learning how to be good test takers.

It's just not possible to do a good job without the right tools. Test-taking strategies are tools to help you perform well on tests. Everyone needs good tools and strategies when facing a problem. If you do not have these, even the smartest or most talented person will do poorly. Think about people who are "wizards" at fixing cars and trucks. Your family's car "dies" in the middle of the road. The situation looks pretty hopeless. How are you ever going to get to that basketball game tomorrow if your parent's car is a mechanical mess? Suddenly, "magic" happens. The mechanic at the repair shop calls your parents and tells them the car is ready, just a day after it broke down. How did this happen? It happened because the auto-repair mechanic had a great deal of knowledge about cars. Most importantly, he had the right tools and strategies to fix the car. He knew how to look at the problem, and when he figured out what to do, he had some special gadgets to get the job done. You also can find special ways that will help you be a successful test taker.

Tools You Can Use on Tests Throughout Your Life!

Be An "Active Learner."

You can't learn anything by being a "sponge." Just because you are sitting in a pool of learning (your classroom) does not mean you are going to learn anything just by being there. Instead, students learn when they actively think and participate during the school day. Students who are active learners pay attention to what is being said. They also constantly ask themselves and their teachers questions about the subject. When able, they participate by making comments and joining discussions. Active learners enjoy school, learn more, feel good about themselves, and usually do better on tests. Remember the auto-repair mechanic? That person had a lot of knowledge about fixing cars. All the tools and strategies in the world will not help unless you have benefited from what your teachers have tried to share.

Being an active learner takes time and practice. If you are the type of student who is easily bored or frustrated, it is going to take some practice to use your classroom time differently. Ask yourself the following questions.

- Am I looking at the teacher?
- Do I pay attention to what is being said?
- Do I have any questions or ideas about what the teacher is saying?
- Do I listen to what my fellow students are saying and think about their ideas?
- Do I work with others to try to solve difficult problems?
- Do I look at the clock and wonder what time school will be over, or do I appreciate what is happening during the school day and how much I can learn?
- Do I try to think about how my schoolwork might be helpful to me now or in the future?

Although you do need special tools and strategies to do well on tests, the more you learn, the better chance you have of doing well on tests. Think about Kristen.

There was a young girl named Kristen,
Who was bored and wouldn't listen.
She didn't train
To use her smart brain
And never knew what she was missing!

Don't Depend on Luck.

Preparing for your state proficiency test might feel stressful or boring at times, but it is an important part of learning how to show what you know and doing your best. Even the smartest student needs to spend time taking practice tests and listening to the advice of teachers about how to do well. Luck alone is not going to help you do well on tests. People who depend on luck do not take responsibility for themselves. Some people who believe in luck do not want to take the time and effort to do well. It is easier for them to say, "It's not my fault I did poorly. It's just not my lucky day." Some people just do not feel very good about their abilities. They get in the habit of saying, "Whatever happens will happen." They believe they can never do well no matter how much they practice or prepare. Students who feel they have no control over what happens to them usually have poor grades and do not feel very good about themselves.

Your performance on tests is not going to be controlled by luck. Instead, you can have a lot of control over how well you do in many areas of your life, including test taking. Don't be like Chuck.

There was a cool boy named Chuck,
Who thought taking tests was just luck.
He never prepared.
He said, "I'm not scared."
When his test scores appear, he should duck!

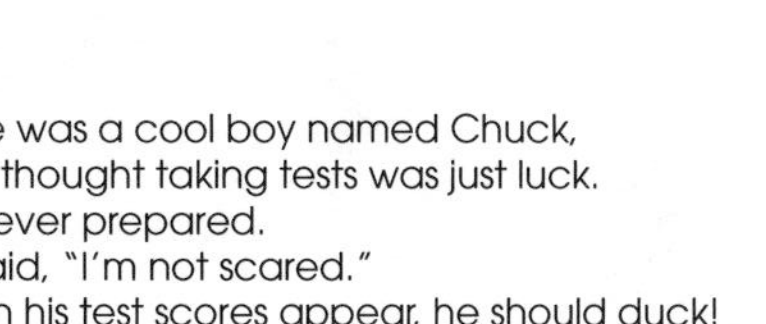

Do Your Best Every Day.

Many students find sixth grade much different than other grades. Suddenly, the work seems really hard. Not only that, but your teachers are no longer treating you like a baby. That's good in some ways, because it gives you more freedom and responsibility, but there sure is a lot to learn. You might feel the same way about tests; you may feel you'll never be prepared. Many times when we are faced with new challenges, it is easy just to give up.

Students are surprised when they find that if they just set small goals for themselves, they can learn an amazing amount. If you learn just one new fact every day of the year, at the end of the year, you will know 365 new facts. You could use those to impress your friends and family. Now think about what would happen if you learned three new facts every day. At the end of the year, you would have learned 1,095 new facts. Soon you will be on your way to having a mind like an encyclopedia.

When you think about a test or any other academic challenge, try to focus on what you can learn step by step and day by day. You will be surprised how all of this learning adds up to make you one of the smartest sixth graders ever. Think about Ray.

There was a smart boy named Ray,
Who learned something new every day.
He was pretty impressed
With what his mind could possess.
His excellent scores were his pay!

Get to Know the Test.

Most sixth graders are probably pretty used to riding in their parents' cars. They know how to make the air-conditioning cooler or warmer, how to change the radio stations, and how to adjust the volume on the radio. Think about being a passenger in a totally unfamiliar car. You might think, "What are all those buttons? How do I even turn on the air conditioner? How do I make the window go up and down?" Now, think about taking your state proficiency test. Your state proficiency test is a test, but it may be different than some tests you have taken in the past. The more familiar you are with the types of questions on the test and how to record your answers, the better you will do. Working through the reading chapters in this book will help you get to know the test. Becoming familiar with the test is a great test-taking tool. Think about Sue.

There was a kid named Sue,
Who thought her test looked new.
"I never saw this before!
How'd I get a bad score?"
If she practiced, she might have a clue!

Read Directions and Questions Carefully!
One of the worst mistakes a student can make on a test is to ignore directions or to read questions carelessly. By the time some students are in the sixth grade, they think they have heard every direction or question ever invented, and it is easy for them to "tune out" directions. Telling yourself, "These directions are just like other directions," or "I'm not really going to take time to read this question because I know what the question will be," are not good test-taking strategies. It is impossible to do well on any test without knowing what is being asked.

Reading directions and questions slowly, repeating them to yourself, and asking yourself if what you are reading makes sense are powerful test-taking strategies. Think about Fred.

There was a nice boy named Fred,
Who ignored almost all that he read.
The directions were easy,
But he said, "I don't need these!"
He should have read them instead.

Know How to Fill in Those Answer Bubbles!
Most sixth graders have taken tests that ask them to fill in answer bubbles. You might be a very bright sixth grader, but you will never "show what you know" unless you fill in the answer bubbles correctly. Don't forget: a computer will be "reading" your multiple-choice question answers. If you do not fill in the answer bubble darkly or if you use a check mark or dot instead of a dark mark, your smart thinking will not be counted. Look at the examples given below.

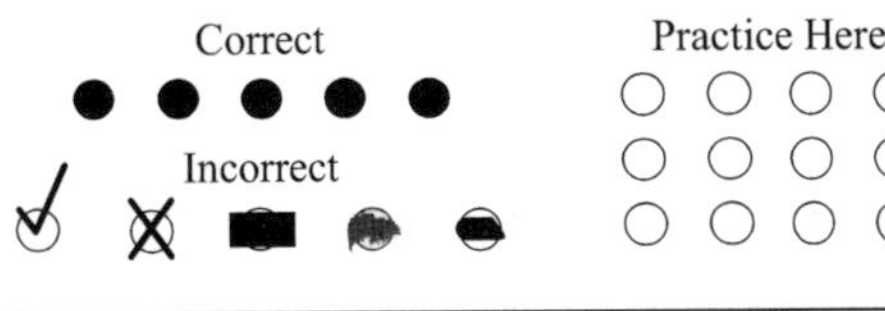

Learning how to fill in answer bubbles takes practice, practice, and more practice. It may not be how you are used to answering multiple-choice questions, but it is the only way to give a right answer on your state proficiency test. Think about Kay!

A stubborn girl named Kay,
Liked to answer questions her own way.
So her marked answer bubbles,
Gave her all sorts of troubles.
Her test scores ruined her day!

Speeding Through the Test Doesn't Help.
Most students have more than enough time to read and answer all the questions on a test. There will always be some students who finish the test more quickly than others, but this does not mean the test was easier for them or their answers are correct. Whether you finish at a faster rate or at a slower rate than other students in your class is not important. As long as you take your time, are well prepared, concentrate on the test, and use some of the skills in this book, you should be able to do just fine. You will not get a better score just because you finish the test before everyone else. Speeding through a test item or through a whole test does not help you do well. In fact, students do their best when they work at a medium rate of speed, not too slow and not too fast. Students who work too slowly tend to get worried about their answers and sometimes change correct answers into incorrect ones. Students who work too fast often make careless mistakes, and many of them do not read directions or questions carefully. Think about Liz.

There was a seventh grader named Liz,
Who sped through her test like a whiz.
She thought she should race
At a very fast pace,
But it caused her to mess up her quiz.

Answer Every Question.
There is no reason that you should not attempt to answer every question you encounter on a test. Even if you don't know the answer, there are ways for you to increase your chances of choosing the correct response. Use the helpful strategies described below to help you answer every question to the best of your ability.

- **If you don't know the answer, guess.**
  Did you know that on your state proficiency test there is no penalty for guessing? That is really good news. That means you have a one out of four chance of getting a multiple-choice question right, even if you just close your eyes and guess. That means that for every four questions you guess, you should get about 25% (1 out of 4) of the questions right. Guessing alone is not going to make you a star on the test, but leaving multiple-choice items blank is not going to help you either.

  Now comes the exciting part. If you can rule out one of the four answer choices, your chances of answering correctly are now one out of three. You can almost see your test score improving right before your eyes.

  Although it is always better to be prepared for the test and to study in school, we all have to guess at one time or another. Some of us do not like to guess because we are afraid of choosing the wrong answer, but on a test, it is better to guess than leave an answer blank. Think about Jess.

There was a smart girl named Jess,
Who thought it was useless to guess.
If a question was tough,
She just gave up.
This only added to her stress.

- **Use a "code" to help you make good guesses.**
  Some students use a "code" to rate each answer when they feel they might have to guess. Using your pencil in the test booklet, you can mark the following codes next to each multiple-choice response so you can make the best possible guess. The codes are as follows:

(+) Putting a "plus sign" by your answer means you are not sure if this answer is correct, but you think this answer is probably more correct than the others.

(?) Putting a "question mark" by your answer means you are unsure if this is the correct answer, but you don't want to rule it out completely.

(–) Putting a "minus sign" by your answer means you are pretty sure this is the wrong answer. You should then choose from the other answers to make an educated guess.

Remember, it is fine to write in your test booklet. Think about Dwight.

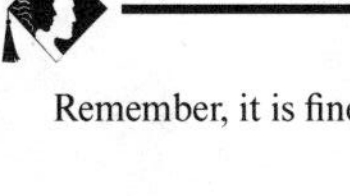

There was a smart kid named Dwight,
Who marked answers that looked to be right.
He'd put a plus sign
Or a dash or a line.
Now the whole world knows he is bright!

- **Use what you know to "power guess."**
  Not everything you know was learned in a classroom. Part of what you know comes from just living your life. When you take a test, you should use everything you have learned in school, but you should also use your experiences outside the classroom to help you answer questions correctly. Using your "common sense," as well as other information you know, will help you do especially well on a test. Try to use what you know from the world around you to eliminate obviously wrong answers. If you can rule out just one answer that you are certain is not correct, you are going to greatly increase your chances of guessing another answer correctly. For example, if you are given a question in which you are asked the definition of a word, and one of the answers reminds you of something you saw on TV, you might be able to count that answer out using your own experiences. Although the reading might be difficult for you, your common sense has eliminated one likely wrong answer. Think about Drew.

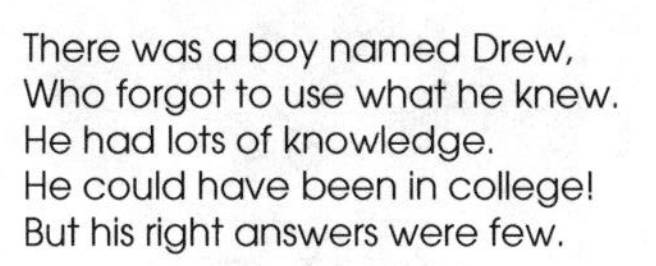

There was a boy named Drew,
Who forgot to use what he knew.
He had lots of knowledge.
He could have been in college!
But his right answers were few.

- **Do Not Get Stuck on One Question.**
  One of the worst things you can do on a test is to get stuck on one question. Your state proficiency test gives you many chances to show all that you have learned. Not knowing the answer to one or two questions is not going to hurt your test results very much.

  When you become stuck on a question, your mind plays tricks on you. You begin to think that you are a total failure, and your worries become greater and greater. This worrying gets in the way of your doing well on the rest of the test. Remember, very few students know all the answers on a test. If you are not sure of the answer after spending some time on it, mark it in your test booklet and come back to it later. When you come back to that question later, you might find a new way of thinking. Sometimes, another question or answer later in the test will remind you of a possible answer to the question that had seemed difficult. If not, you can use your guessing strategies to solve the questions you are unsure of after you have answered all the questions you know. Also, when you move on from a troubling question and find you are able to answer other questions correctly, you will feel much better about yourself and you will feel calmer. This will help you have a better chance of succeeding on a question that made you feel "stuck." Think about Von.

There was a sweet girl named Von,
Who got stuck and just couldn't go on.
She'd sit there and stare,
But the answer wasn't there.
Before she knew it, all the time was gone.

- **Always, and This Means Always, Recheck Your Work.**
  Everyone makes mistakes. People make the most mistakes when they feel a little worried or rushed. Checking your work is a very important part of doing your best. This is particularly true in the reading section, where careless mistakes can lead to a wrong answer. Going back and rechecking your answers is very important. You can read a paragraph over again if there is something you do not understand or something that you forgot. If an answer does not seem to make sense, go back and reread the question. Think about Jen.

There was a quick girl named Jen,
Who read stuff once and never again.
It would have been nice
If she'd reread it twice.
Her test scores would be better then!

- **Pay Attention to Yourself and Not Others.**
  It is easy to look around the room and wonder how friends are doing. However, it is important to think about how you are using tools and strategies. Don't become distracted by friends. You are going to waste a lot of time if you try to figure out what your friends are doing. Instead, use that time to "show what you know."

  If it becomes hard for you to pay attention, give yourself a little break. If you feel you are getting a little tense or worried, or if a question seems tough, close your eyes for a second or two. Think positive thoughts. Try to put negative thoughts out of your mind. You might want to stretch your arms or feet or move around a little to help you focus. Anything you may do to help pay better attention to the test is a great test-taking strategy. Think about Kirk.

There was a boy named Kirk,
Who thought of everything but his work.
He stared into the air
And squirmed in his chair.
When his test scores come, he won't look!

General Test-Taking Strategies for Reading

There are multiple-choice and short-answer questions on the Reading Assessment in this workbook. Here are some good strategies to use on the Reading Assessment.

- **Read the Question Carefully.**

  It may help to look over the questions before you read through the passage. As you read the passage, look for information that may help you answer the questions.

- **Look for Keywords.**

  Remember, you can write in your test booklet. As you read through the different passages, circle or underline important words you come across. Make notes in the margin with ideas that seem to answer the question.

- **Review What You Read to Find More Details.**

  If you don't think you can answer the question, reread the passage and look for more details.

- **Ask Yourself, "Did I Answer the Question?"**

  Read the answer choice you think is correct to make sure you have answered the question correctly.

- **Circle the Numbers of the Questions You Cannot Answer.**

  If you are not sure of the correct answer, circle the question number and return to it later in the test.

- **Do Not Immediately Pick Your First Answer.**

  Your first choice could be the correct choice, but it could also be a wrong answer that a test maker used to distract you. Recheck your answers.

Specific Strategies for Online Tests

Kids usually have two different kinds of thoughts about taking a test on a computer. Some say, "Well, I use my computer all the time … I'm not going to even pay attention to the test … computers are easy!" Some kids think in the opposite way. They say, "A computer test? That has to be even scarier than a regular test … there is no way I am going to do well!" The truth is that both of them are wrong. You have to use some special strategies to do your best on computer tests, and when you do, you will do your best!

1. **Read the Directions.** Here is a silly question: Would you want to eat a cake your friend made if he didn't read the directions on the box? Probably not! But even if you aren't a famous cook, you could make a pretty good cake if you read and follow directions. If you read the directions for EACH QUESTION you will have a much better chance of showing what you know. Because even if you know a lot, you have to answer what the question asks. Don't leave out this important step to test success!

2. **Don't Go With the First Answer.** Take a little time and read the WHOLE question and ALL the answer choices. The first answer that looks right is not always the best. Think about going out to dinner with your grandmother. You look at the menu and see "Big Ole Burger"! That sounds good. But if you looked at ALL the menu choices, you might have found your favorite tacos! The burger was good, but if you took more time, you would have found a better choice.

3. **Ask Yourself … How Much Time Do I Have?** You will have a certain amount of time to complete each section of the test. Always check to see how much time you will have. Practice also helps. Did you know that football players practice and practice to see how long it takes to line up and start a play? After a while they are more relaxed and don't worry about time running out. You need to take some practice tests to feel comfortable with timed tests.

4. **Is There a Good Way to Guess?** Most of the time it is a good idea to guess, especially if you can make an "educated" guess! That means you know some things about the question, but not everything. Remember to use your common sense, as well as other information you know, to help you make an "educated guess."

5. **When Should You Guess?** Unless the directions say that you will lose points for guessing, go for it! Educated guesses are the best, but even if you are really unsure of the answer, calm down and take a guess. If you have four possible answers, and make a guess, you have a one out of four chance of guessing correctly. That is like having three old pennies and one new penny in a bowl. If you just reach in, you will get the new penny one out of every four times you try. That's why you should answer every question!

6. **Don't Mess With That Test Window!** When people get a little nervous, they tend to make silly mistakes. One kid was rushing to make some toast before running off to school, and he unplugged the toaster instead of making the toast! Figure out how the computer screen works, and DON'T close that test window!

7. **Have a Good Attitude!** The better you feel, the better you will do! Remind yourself of how much you have learned in school. Remember that while this test is important, your teachers will still like you a lot no matter how you do. Just do your best and feel good about yourself. Did you know that when runners have a good attitude, that they win more often? Well, the same goes for you and tests!

8. **If You Have Time Left, Use It!** You can use extra time to help you do your best! If your computer test allows, review your answers, especially if you guessed on a question or two. Take a deep breath and calm down. You might find that a better answer comes into your mind. Talk to yourself a little about some of your answers. You might ask yourself, "I chose the answer that said that it will take 6 hours for that ice cube to melt. That seems like a long time … maybe I better recheck this and see if that makes sense."

Sixth graders all over have good ideas about tests. Here are some of them!

- Ask yourself, "Did I answer the question that was asked?" Carefully read the question so you can give the right answer.
- Read each answer choice before filling in an answer bubble. Sometimes, you read the first choice, and it seems right. But, when you get to the third choice, you realize that's the correct answer. If you had stopped with the first choice, you would have answered the question incorrectly. It is important to read all four choices before answering the question.
- Remember, nobody is trying to trick you. Do not look for trick answers. There will always be a right answer. If the answer choices do not look right, mark the question and go back to it later.
- Don't look around the room. Don't worry about how fast your friends are working, and don't worry about how well they are doing. Only worry about yourself. If you do that, you will do better on the test.

Reading

Introduction

The Reading assessment reflects what students should know and should be able to do in the sixth grade. State assessments assess students' knowledge with multiple-choice and constructed-response items. The questions are not meant to confuse or trick them but are written so students have the best opportunity to show what they know about reading.

The Reading chapter in the *Show What You Know® on the Common Core for Grade 6 Reading, Parent/Teacher Edition,* contains the following:

- The Common Core State Standards for Grade 6.
- Two full-length Reading Assessments from the Student Workbook, in reduced-page format, with sample responses, correlation charts, a standards checklist, and a grading document.

Reading Standards for Literature (RL)

The following standards offer a focus for instruction each year and help ensure that students gain adequate exposure to a range of texts and tasks. Rigor is also infused through the requirement that students read increasingly complex texts through the grades. Students advancing through the grades are expected to meet each year's grade-specific standards and retain or further develop skills and understandings mastered in preceding grades.

Key Ideas and Details

1. Cite textual evidence to support analysis of what the text says explicitly as well as inferences drawn from the text.
2. Determine a theme or central idea of a text and how it is conveyed through particular details; provide a summary of the text distinct from personal opinions or judgments.
3. Describe how a particular story's or drama's plot unfolds in a series of episodes as well as how the characters respond or change as the plot moves toward a resolution.

Craft and Structure

4. Determine the meaning of words and phrases as they are used in a text, including figurative and connotative meanings; analyze the impact of a specific word choice on meaning and tone.
5. Analyze how a particular sentence, chapter, scene, or stanza fits into the overall structure of a text and contributes to the development of the theme, setting, or plot.
6. Explain how an author develops the point of view of the narrator or speaker in a text.

Integration of Knowledge and Ideas

7. Compare and contrast the experience of reading a story, drama, or poem to listening to or viewing an audio, video, or live version of the text, including contrasting what they "see" and "hear" when reading the text to what they perceive when they listen or watch.
8. (Not applicable to literature)
9. Compare and contrast texts in different forms or genres (e.g., stories and poems; historical novels and fantasy stories) in terms of their approaches to similar themes and topics.

Range of Reading and Level of Text Complexity

10. By the end of the year, read and comprehend literature, including stories, dramas, and poems, in the grades 6–8 text complexity band proficiently, with scaffolding as needed at the high end of the range.

Copying is Prohibited
© Englefield & Associates, Inc.

Reading Standards for Informational Text (RI)

Key Ideas and Details

1. Cite textual evidence to support analysis of what the text says explicitly as well as inferences drawn from the text.
2. Determine a central idea of a text and how it is conveyed through particular details; provide a summary of the text distinct from personal opinions or judgments.
3. Analyze in detail how a key individual, event, or idea is introduced, illustrated, and elaborated in a text (e.g., through examples or anecdotes).

Craft and Structure

4. Determine the meaning of words and phrases as they are used in a text, including figurative, connotative, and technical meanings.
5. Analyze how a particular sentence, paragraph, chapter, or section fits into the overall structure of a text and contributes to the development of the ideas.
6. Determine an author's point of view or purpose in a text and explain how it is conveyed in the text.

Integration of Knowledge and Ideas

7. Integrate information presented in different media or formats (e.g., visually, quantitatively) as well as in words to develop a coherent understanding of a topic or issue.
8. Trace and evaluate the argument and specific claims in a text, distinguishing claims that are supported by reasons and evidence from claims that are not.
9. Compare and contrast one author's presentation of events with that of another (e.g., a memoir written by and a biography on the same person).

Range of Reading and Level of Text Complexity

10. By the end of the year, read and comprehend literary nonfiction in the grades 6–8 text complexity band proficiently, with scaffolding as needed at the high end of the range.

Glossary

alliteration: Repeating the same sound at the beginning of several words in a phrase or sentence. For example, "The bees buzzed in the back of the blue barn."

adjectives: Words that describe nouns.

adverbs: Words that describe verbs.

antonyms: Words that mean the opposite (e.g., *light* is an antonym of *dark*).

audience: The people who read a written piece or hear the piece being read.

author's purpose: The reason an author writes, such as to entertain, to inform, or to persuade.

author's tone: The attitude the writer takes toward an audience, a subject, or a character. Tone is shown through the writer's choice of words and details. Examples of tone are happy, sad, angry, gentle, etc.

base word (also called root word): The central part of a word that other word parts may be attached to.

biography: A true story about a person's life.

cause: The reason for an action, feeling, or response.

character: A person or an animal in a story, play, or other literary work.

compare: To use examples to show how things are alike.

contrast: To use examples to show how things are different.

details: Many small parts which help to tell a story.

descriptive text: To create a clear picture of a person, place, thing, or idea by using vivid words.

directions: An order or instructions on how to do something or how to act.

draw conclusion: To make a decision or form an opinion after considering the facts from the text.

effect: A result of a cause.

events: Things that happen.

fact: An actual happening or truth.

fiction: A passage that is made up rather than factually true. Examples of fiction are novels and short stories.

format: The way a published piece of writing looks, including the font, legibility, spacing, margins, and white space.

generalize: To come to a broad idea or rule about something after considering particular facts.

genres: Categories of literary and informational works (e.g., biography, mystery, historical fiction, poetry).

graphic organizer: Any illustration, chart, table, diagram, map, etc., used to help interpret information about the text.

heading: A word or group of words at the top or front of a piece of writing.

infer: To make a guess based on facts and observations.

inference: An important idea or conclusion drawn from reasoning rather than directly stated in the text.

inform: To give knowledge; to tell.

informational text (also called expository text): Text with the purpose of telling about details, facts, and information that is true (nonfiction). Informational text is found in textbooks, encyclopedias, biographies, and newspaper articles.

literary devices: Techniques used to convey an author's message or voice (e.g., figurative language, simile, metaphors, etc.).

literary text (also called narrative text): Text that describes actions or events, usually written as fiction. Examples are novels and short stories.

main idea: The main reason the passage was written; every passage has a main idea. Usually you can find the main idea in the topic sentence of the paragraph.

metaphor: A comparison between two unlike things without using the words "like" or "as." An example of a metaphor is, "My bedroom is a junkyard!"

 Copying is Prohibited © Englefield & Associates, Inc.

Glossary

mood: The feeling or emotion the reader gets from a piece of writing.

nonfiction: A passage of writing that tells about real people, events, and places without changing any facts. Examples of nonfiction are an autobiography, a biography, an essay, a newspaper article, a magazine article, a personal diary, and a letter.

onomatopoeia: The use of words in which the sound of the word suggests the sound associated with it. For example, buzz, hiss, splat.

opinion: What one thinks about something or somebody; an opinion is not necessarily based on facts. Feelings and experiences usually help a person form an opinion.

passage: A passage or writing that may be fiction (literary/narrative) or nonfiction (informational/expository).

persuade: To cause to do something by using reason or argument; to cause to believe something.

plan: A method of doing something that has been thought out ahead of time.

plot: A series of events that make up a story. Plot tells "what happens" in a story, novel, or narrative poem.

plot sequence: The order of events in a story.

poetry: A type of writing that uses images and patterns to express feelings.

point of view: The way a story is told; it could be in first person, omniscient, or in third person.

predict: The ability of the reader to know or expect that something is going to happen in a text before it does.

prefix: A group of letters added to the beginning of a word. For example, *un*tie, *re*build, *pre*teen.

preposition: A word that links another word or group of words to other parts of the sentence. Examples are in, on, of, at, by, between, outside, etc.

problem: An issue or question in a text that needs to be answered.

published work: The final writing draft shared with the audience.

reliable: Sources used for writing that are trustworthy.

resource: A source of help or support.

rhyme: When words have the same last sound. For example, hat/cat, most/toast, ball/call.

root word (also called base word): The central part of a word that other word parts may be attached to.

schema: The accumulated knowledge that a person can draw from life experiences to help understand concepts, roles, emotions, and events.

sentence: A group of words that express a complete thought. It has a subject and a verb.

sequential order: The arrangement or ordering of information, content, or ideas (e.g., a story told in chronological order describes what happened first, then second, then third, etc.).

setting: The time and place of a story or play. The setting helps to create the mood in a story, such as inside a spooky house or inside a shopping mall during the holidays.

simile: A comparison between two unlike things, using the words "like" or "as." "Her eyes are as big as saucers" is an example of a simile.

solution: An answer to a problem.

stanzas: Lines of poetry grouped together.

story: An account of something that happened.

story elements: The important parts of the story, including characters, setting, plot, problem, and solution.

style: A way of writing that is individual to the writer, such as the writer's choice of words, phrases, and images.

suffix: A group of letters added to the end of a word. For example, teach*er*, color*ful*, sugar*less*, etc.

summary: To retell what happens in a story in a short way by telling the main ideas, not details.

Glossary

supporting details: Statements that often follow the main idea. Supporting details give you more information about the main idea.

symbolism: Something that represents something else. For example, a dove is a symbol for peace.

synonyms: Words with the same, or almost the same, meaning (e.g., *sketch* is a synonym of *draw*).

theme: The major idea or topic that the author reveals in a literary work. A theme is usually not stated directly in the work. Instead, the reader has to think about all the details of the work and then make an inference (an educated guess) about what they all mean.

title: A name of a book, film, play, piece of music, or other work of art.

tone: A way of writing that shows a feeling.

topic sentence: A sentence that states the main idea of the paragraph.

valid: Correct, acceptable.

verb: A word that shows action or being.

voice: To express a choice or opinion.

Copying is Prohibited © Englefield & Associates, Inc.

Reading Assessment One

Responses *Throughout this section, pages from Reading Assessment One of the Student Workbook are included in reduced-page format. Correct multiple-choice answers and sample responses for each constructed-response item are indicated.*

Directions:

This Grade 6 Reading Assessment has multiple-choice and short-answer questions.

There are several important things to remember as you take this test:

- Read each multiple-choice question carefully. Think about what is being asked. Then fill in one answer bubble to mark your answer.
- If you do not know the answer to a multiple-choice question, skip it and go on. If you have time, go back to the questions you skipped and answer them.
- For short-answer questions, write your response clearly and neatly in the box provided.
- If you finish the Assessment early, go back and check over your work.

Directions for Taking the Reading Assessment

The Reading Assessment contains eight reading selections and 40 questions. Some of the selections are fiction, while others are nonfiction. Read each selection and the questions that follow carefully. You may look back at any selection as many times as you would like. If you are unsure of a question, you can move to the next question, and go back to the question you skipped later.

Multiple-choice questions require you to pick the best answer out of four possible choices. Only one answer is correct. The short-answer questions will ask you to write your answer and explain your thinking using words. Remember to read the questions and the answer choices carefully. You will mark your answers on the answer document.

When you finish, check your answers.

© Englefield & Associates, Inc. Copying is Prohibited Student Workbook 29

Read this selection. Then answer the questions that follow.

Birches

by Robert Frost

When I see birches bend to left and right
Across the lines of straighter darker trees,
I like to think some boy's been swinging them.
But swinging doesn't bend them down to stay.
Ice-storms do that. Often you must have seen them
Loaded with ice a sunny winter morning
After a rain. They click upon themselves
As the breeze rises, and turn many-colored
As the stir cracks and crazes their enamel.
Soon the sun's warmth makes them shed crystal shells
Shattering and avalanching on the snow-crust—
Such heaps of broken glass to sweep away
You'd think the inner dome of heaven had fallen.
They are dragged to the withered bracken[1] by the load,
And they seem not to break; though once they are bowed
So low for long, they never right themselves:
You may see their trunks arching in the woods
Years afterwards, trailing their leaves on the ground

[1] **bracken:** a large course fern

Go On

Like girls on hands and knees that throw their hair
Before them over their heads to dry in the sun.
But I was going to say when Truth broke in
With all her matter-of-fact about the ice-storm
(Now am I free to be poetical[2]?)
I should prefer to have some boy bend them
As he went out and in to fetch the cows—
Some boy too far from town to learn baseball,
Whose only play was what he found himself,
Summer or winter, and could play alone.
One by one he subdued his father's trees
By riding them down over and over again
Until he took the stiffness out of them,
And not one but hung limp, not one was left
For him to conquer. He learned all there was
To learn about not launching out too soon
And so not carrying the tree away
Clear to the ground. He always kept his poise
To the top branches, climbing carefully
With the same pains you use to fill a cup
Up to the brim, and even above the brim.
Then he flung outward, feet first, with a swish,
Kicking his way down through the air to the ground.
So was I once myself a swinger of birches.
And so I dream of going back to be.
It's when I'm weary of considerations,
And life is too much like a pathless wood
Where your face burns and tickles with the cobwebs
Broken across it, and one eye is weeping
From a twig's having lashed across it open.
I'd like to get away from earth awhile
And then come back to it and start over.
May no fate willfully misunderstand me
And half grant what I wish and snatch me away

[2] **poetical:** skilled or fond of poetry

Go On

Not to return. Earth's the right place for love:
I don't know where it's likely to go better.
I'd like to go by climbing a birch tree,
And climb black branches up a snow-white trunk
Toward heaven, till the tree could bear no more,
But dipped its top and set me down again.
That would be good both going and coming back.
One could do worse than be a swinger of birches.

Go On

1. The poet says, "life is too much like a pathless wood."

   What does the poet mean when he compares life to a pathless wood?

   A. You are free to make your own decisions.

   X **B.** You must overcome obstacles in order to move forward.

   C. You might be paralyzed with indecision.

   D. Your choices are unlimited.

2. How are the narrator and the imaginary young boy in the poem similar?

   X **A.** Both are swingers of birches.

   B. Both live in the country.

   C. Both like to watch how the birch trees' branches change after ice storms.

   D. Both like to have fun and don't worry too much about the world.

3. Read these lines from the poem, *Birches*.

   > "They click upon themselves
   > As the breeze rises, and turn many-colored
   > As the stir cracks and crazes their enamel."

   Why does the poet include alliteration in these lines?

   X **A.** to make the reader hear the ice on the branches

   B. to make the reader see the ice on the branches

   C. to make the reader smell the ice on the branches

   D. to make the reader feel the ice on the branches

4. What word BEST describes the narrator in the poem?

   A. excited

   B. hopeful

   C. afraid

   X **D.** longing

Go On

5. Which two objects does the poet compare using a simile?

A. birches and ice storms

X B. birches and girls drying their hair in the sun

C. birches and boys who swing in trees

D. birches and boys who play baseball

6. In your own words, tell why the poet dreams of going back to being a "swinger of birches."

Support your answer with **two** details from the poem.

Short-answer responses may vary. The poet dreams of going back to being a swinger of birches whenever he is "weary of considerations." He sees swinging on birch trees as a temporary escape from the cares of the world.

Go On

Read this selection. Then answer the questions that follow.

Cozumel, Mexico

An Island Paradise

1 What if you could visit a place that offers clear blue water, crystal beaches, and underwater adventures? Cozumel, in Mexico, is just such a place. Located off Mexico's Yucatan Peninsula, Cozumel has become a favorite vacation spot for divers and those who love the outdoors.

2 This exciting island is only 10 miles long and 28 miles wide, but it is Mexico's largest island. It attracts many visitors from across the globe each year. Most people travel to Cozumel to experience underwater diving at its best. It is thought of as one of the best diving spots in the world, second only to Australia.

3 Snorkeling is another activity Cozumel visitors enjoy. It is the second most popular water sport on the island. Beginners can snorkel right off the beaches of the hotels and see a variety of fish without going out too far. Another good place for beginning snorkelers is Chankanaab National Park. This park has shallow reefs that attract fish of all shapes, colors, and sizes.

4 If you're not interested in water sports, the Chankanaab Park also has nature trails where visitors can spend time walking and admiring the different plants of the island. You might even spot an iguana or two taking an afternoon nap in the sun!

5 San Miguel is the only town in Cozumel. Tourists from cruise ships and others who make the trip to town are in for a real treat. There are plenty of people who live in the town selling T-shirts, silver jewelry, and other goods made in Mexico.

6 It's easy to see why Cozumel is a favorite choice for outdoor adventures and sun-filled excitement!

Go On

Cozumel

7 Nestled between the trade routes to and from Honduras and Veracruz, Cozumel was well positioned as a seaport. Settled as early as 300 AD by the Mayas, this island served many purposes. These purposes included being a pilgrimage site (a sacred place people journey to) and the center for Mayan trade.

8 As the Spanish arrived in the area in the late 1400s and early 1500s, the Mayas resisted a number of attempts at Spanish settlement. By 1519, however, a bitter struggle for the Yucatan Peninsula began. Slowly, the struggle crept outward. A Spanish presence began to take over the island. With the arrival of Hernan Cortéz and his men, many of the Mayan temples and shrines were destroyed. The foreigners also exposed the natives to smallpox. An epidemic (a very fast and wide spread of an illness) broke out, and by 1570, Cozumel's population declined to fewer than 300 people.

9 Throughout the 17th century, Cozumel was occupied mainly by pirates. The location of the island provided privacy and protection from danger. The area wasn't re-inhabited until 1848. At that time, Spanish settlers sought refuge from the Caste War, which was being fought on the mainland. A quiet fishing village was eventually established, and Cozumel remained as such until 1961. In that year, French explorer Jacques Cousteau declared the area's waters to be some of the most amazing for exploration. Since then, Cozumel has become a popular tourist destination, welcoming visitors from around the world every year.

Go On

7. How are the two sections of the selection, "An Island Paradise" and "Cozumel" similar?

   A. Both sections mention that San Miguel is a popular tourist destination.

   B. Both sections talk about pirates living on Cozumel.

   X**C.** Both sections mention that Cozumel is a popular tourist destination.

   D. Both sections talk about Cozumel's position as a seaport.

8. How are the two sections of the selection different in their approaches to writing about Cozumel?

   A. "An Island Paradise" talks about the history of Cozumel; "Cozumel" talks about the island in the present.

   X**B.** "An Island Paradise" talks about Cozumel in the present; "Cozumel" talks about the history of the island.

   C. "An Island Paradise" talks about Cozumel in the present; "Cozumel" talks about the future of the island.

   D. "An Island Paradise" talks about Cozumel in the future; "Cozumel" talks about the history of the island.

Go On

9. Cozumel was occupied mainly by pirates throughout the 17th century because–

   A. Cozumel was a fishing village.

   B. the island offers snorkeling and shopping.

   C. the location of the island was a pilgrimage site and center for Mayan trade.

   X **D.** the location of the island provided privacy and protection from danger.

10. What is the author's purpose for writing the selection?

    Provide **three** details from the selection to support your answer.

Extended-response answers may vary. The author wrote this selection to give information about Cozumel in the past and present. The first part of the selection describes the present-day highlights of Cozumel. It is a popular tourist destination, attracting many people from all over the world to its beaches. People can snorkel and enjoy other water sports while on vacation. They can also walk on nature trails or go shopping. The author also explains about the history of the island in the second part of the selection. It used to be a pilgrimage site and a center of Mayan trading. The island was once mainly occupied by pirates, and then was taken over by Spanish settlers. After much of the population died from a smallpox epidemic, the island eventually grew into a popular place for tourists.

11. Read the sentence from the selection.

    "In that year, French explorer Jacques Cousteau declared the area's waters to be some of the most amazing for *exploration*."

    What does the word *exploration* mean in the sentence above?

    A. to establish

    B. to determine

    C. to declare

    X **D.** to investigate

Go On

Read this selection. Then answer the questions that follow.

Little Women

by Louisa May Alcott

1 "Christmas won't be Christmas without any presents," grumbled Jo, lying on the rug.

2 "It's so dreadful to be poor!" sighed Meg, looking down at her old dress.

3 "I don't think it's fair for some girls to have plenty of pretty things, and other girls nothing at all," added little Amy, with an injured sniff.

4 "We've got Father and Mother, and each other," said Beth contentedly from her corner.

5 The four young faces on which the firelight shone brightened at the cheerful words, but darkened again as Jo said sadly, "We haven't got Father, and shall not have him for a long time." She didn't say "perhaps never," but each silently added it, thinking of Father far away, where the fighting was.

6 Nobody spoke for a minute; then Meg said in an altered tone, "You know the reason Mother proposed not having any presents this Christmas was because it is going to be a hard winter for everyone; and she thinks we ought not to spend money for pleasure, when our men are suffering so in the army. We can't do much, but we can make our little sacrifices, and ought to do it gladly. But I am afraid I don't," and Meg shook her head, as she thought regretfully of all the pretty things she wanted.

7 "But I don't think the little we should spend would do any good. We've each got a dollar, and the army wouldn't be much helped by our giving that. I agree not to expect anything from Mother or you, but I do want to buy Undine and Sintran for myself. I've wanted it so long," said Jo, who was a bookworm.

Go On

8 “I planned to spend mine in new music,” said Beth, with a little sigh, which no one heard but the hearth brush and kettle-holder.

9 “I shall get a nice box of Faber’s drawing pencils; I really need them,” said Amy decidedly.

10 “Mother didn’t say anything about our money, and she won’t wish us to give up everything. Let’s each buy what we want, and have a little fun; I’m sure we work hard enough to earn it,” cried Jo, examining the heels of her shoes in a gentlemanly manner.

11 “I know I do—teaching those tiresome children nearly all day, when I’m longing to enjoy myself at home,” began Meg, in the complaining tone again.

12 “You don’t have half such a hard time as I do,” said Jo. “How would you like to be shut up for hours with a nervous, fussy old lady, who keeps you trotting, is never satisfied, and worries you till you’re ready to fly out the window or cry?”

13 “It’s naughty to fret, but I do think washing dishes and keeping things tidy is the worst work in the world. It makes me cross, and my hands get so stiff, I can’t practice well at all.” And Beth looked at her rough hands with a sigh that any one could hear that time.

14 “I don’t believe any of you suffer as I do,” cried Amy, “for you don’t have to go to school with impertinent girls, who plague you if you don’t know your lessons, and laugh at your dresses, and label your father if he isn’t rich, and insult you when your nose isn’t nice.”

15 “If you mean libel, I’d say so, and not talk about labels, as if Papa was a pickle bottle,” advised Jo, laughing.

16 “I know what I mean, and you needn’t be satirical about it. It’s proper to use good words, and improve your vocabulary,” returned Amy, with dignity.

17 “Don’t peck at one another, children. Don’t you wish we had the money Papa lost when we were little, Jo? Dear me! How happy and good we’d be, if we had no worries!” said Meg, who could remember better times.

18 “You said the other day you thought we were a deal happier than the King children, for they were fighting and fretting all the time, in spite of their money.”

19 “So I did, Beth. Well, I think we are. For though we do have to work, we make fun of ourselves, and are a pretty jolly set, as Jo would say.”

Go On

12. Read the sentence from the selection, “Little Women.”

“She didn’t say ‘perhaps never,’ but each silently added it, thinking of Father far away, where the fighting was.”

What point of view does the sentence above illustrate?

A. first person

B. second person

C. third person

X D. omniscient

13. Read the sentence from the selection, “Little Women.”

“Christmas won’t be Christmas without any presents,” *grumbled* Jo, lying on the rug.

What mood does the author create by using the word *grumbled*?

X A. The author creates an angry mood by using the word *grumbled*.

B. The author creates a sad mood by using the word *grumbled*.

C. The author creates a happy mood by using the word *grumbled*.

D. The author creates a nervous mood by using the word *grumbled*.

Go On

14. Which of the following sentences best summarizes the selection "Little Women"?

A. The sisters complain to each other about their jobs.

B. The sisters discuss whether or not they should buy presents for Christmas.

X C. The sisters' differing personalities are revealed in their reactions to the prospect of not having presents for Christmas.

D. The sisters tell each other about the presents they want for Christmas.

15. Which setting feature is associated with the changing mood in the girls' conversation?

A. the snowstorm outside

X B. the firelight

C. the sunlight

D. the temperature of the room

Go On

Read this selection. Then answer the questions that follow.

Duke Ellington

(1899 – 1974)

1 Duke Ellington was born Edward Kennedy Ellington on April 29, 1899, in Washington, D.C. His mother and father, Daisy Kennedy Ellington and James Edward Ellington, were kind and loving parents. They enjoyed music and shared their love of the art with their son. During Ellington's youth, many who knew him admired his noble qualities. As a result, they gave him a regal-sounding nickname: "The Duke." Person after person called Ellington "The Duke" and the nickname stuck. Future generations have come to know "The Duke" as one of history's greatest jazz talents.

2 By the age of seven, Ellington was taking piano lessons, but he was not impressed with the instrument, not even a little bit. Instead, Ellington was fascinated by the game of baseball. In fact, for his very first job, he sold packages of peanuts at Washington Senators' baseball games. Although he didn't realize it at the time, this experience made a big impact on Ellington. As a shy kid, he was terrified at the thought of facing large crowds. Selling peanuts at the stadium helped Ellington overcome his fears. He had to get comfortable with large numbers of people in order to sell his peanuts and make money. As time progressed, he grew to like "performing" for the crowds.

3 Even though he didn't like the piano at first, Ellington was slowly drawn to music. To study the arts, he attended the Armstrong Manual Training School, rather than attending a typical high school. During a family trip to Asbury Park in New Jersey, Ellington came to know Harvey Brooks, a dynamic piano player. Brooks was quick to show Ellington his signature piano tricks and shortcuts. Ellington felt Brooks' influence immediately, as Brooks made quite an impression on the young Ellington. Ellington later recalled his experiences with Brooks, "When I got home I had a real yearning to play. I hadn't been able to get off the ground before, but after hearing him I said to myself, 'Man you're going to have to do it.' " From then on, he spent most of his free time listening to ragtime[1] pianists. He was amazed at the way they could charm audiences. He was drawn to their music and charm. Although inspired by their performances, Ellington was able to pound out his own unique style.

Go On

4 Ellington was composing his own works by the age of 17. Throughout his late teens and early twenties, he enjoyed modest success as a professional musician. He was earning enough to make a living, and he was making his way doing something he had grown to love. In 1923, Ellington left Washington, D.C., and headed for New York City. Ellington and his band, The Washingtonians, began recording his music and playing in popular nightclubs. The band was featured regularly on a national radio broadcast titled "From the Cotton Club." The power and beauty of Ellington's work was recognized all over the nation, and his popularity increased.

5 Eventually, Ellington took his band on the road. They played all over the world, from London to Egypt to Los Angeles. Their music was well received as it poured from concert halls, nightclubs, and theaters. Ellington was not only a musician, a bandleader, and a songwriter, he was also a global ambassador for American music.

6 Ellington's talents were honored many times over. The French government presented him with their highest award, the Legion of Honor. The government of the United States granted him its highest civil honor, the Presidential Medal of Freedom. Ellington received honorary degrees from Howard University and Yale University. He was given membership in the American Institute of Arts and Letters, and he was the first jazz musician to become a member of the Royal Music Academy in Stockholm.

7 While Ellington is largely recognized for his contributions to big-band jazz, he had many other achievements. He composed over 1,500 works, and many were featured in musicals, films, television programs, concerts, and ballets. His talents as a composer and as a dynamic performer have kept Ellington's legend alive for almost a century. Duke Ellington died from cancer on May 24, 1974. He is considered one of the greatest musicians of all time. As a tribute to his impact on music, his musical materials are now preserved in the Duke Ellington Collection at the Smithsonian Institute in Washington, D.C.

[1] **ragtime:** American music style popular during the early 1900s; influential in the development of jazz

Go On

16. Which of the following is the best summary of the selection, "Duke Ellington"?

A. Duke Ellington was born in 1899 with the name Edward and was then given the nickname "The Duke." His parents loved music and wanted him to like it, too, so they made him take piano lessons. When Duke was seven, he started selling peanuts at baseball games.

B. Duke Ellington was a musician who learned to play the piano even though he did not enjoy it. He went to a special high school to study the arts instead of going to a regular high school. After high school, he became very popular as a professional musician.

C. Duke Ellington was a musician who played all over the world. He played in cities such as London and Los Angeles. Both the French and the United States governments gave Ellington awards for his music. He died in 1974.

X**D.** Duke Ellington was a musician who did not like the piano at first but learned to love it later on. In his twenties, he became more and more popular as a professional musician. Ellington played all over the world and won many honors. He was also a talented composer, and his materials are preserved in Washington, D.C.

17. Read the sentence from the third paragraph of the selection, "Duke Ellington."

"Even though he didn't like the piano at first, Ellington was slowly *drawn* to music."

The word *drawn* is used to mean Ellington–

A. was an artist as well as a musician.

B. tied in a contest with another musician.

X**C.** was slowly attracted to playing music.

D. looked tired after playing music.

Go On

18. How are Duke Ellington and Harvey Brooks alike?

A. They both sold peanuts at Washington Senators' baseball games.

B. They both took piano lessons from the same teacher.

C. They both received the Legion of Honor from the French government.

X D. They both enjoyed playing the piano.

19. According to the selection, what happened when Ellington saw piano performances by Harvey Brooks?

A. Ellington decided to become a member of the Washingtonians.

B. Ellington started to attend the Armstrong Manual Training School.

X C. Ellington was influenced by Brooks' performance style and Ellington's interest in piano playing had been sparked.

D. Ellington started taking piano lessons from Brooks, who helped Ellington create his own style.

20. How does the author of "Duke Ellington" organize paragraphs 2–4?

A. by telling about problems Ellington had; then telling how he solved those problems

B. by listing all of the things that caused Ellington to become famous

X C. by telling about the first part of Ellington's life in time order

D. by describing the different sounds of Ellington's music

Go On

Read this selection. Then answer the questions that follow.

My Amazing, Dreadful, Horrible Day

1 This morning I slept through my alarm clock, missed my bus, was yelled at by my dad, and left without my packed lunch — and today was "mystery" meatloaf day! Yuck!

2 I got to school, ran through the door, and tripped on my untied shoelaces. I scrapped my knee and had to go to the nurse, who bandaged me up and made me miss the first five minutes of a pop quiz in my English class over last night's homework.

3 I scrambled to write down the answers and turned in my paper with a couple of students still left trying to make up answers to the questions. They obviously did not do the homework the night before. I was glad I did my homework.

4 Just as I was thinking my day might turn around, Sabrina, without question the prettiest girl in class, started giggling and pointed out that my socks did not match. It wasn't even a forgivable black and navy blue mismatch. One sock was lime green with a blue band at the top and the other was white with my name sewn onto the back (thanks to my mom who loves to label everything).

5 I was mortified, but I tried to prove to Sabrina that it didn't bother me, and I pretended to laugh at myself.

Go On

6 I reached into my book bag to retrieve my literature book and hit my elbow right on the "funny bone" making my whole arm tingle and my face contort into unappealing faces.

7 The class laughed at me, and my teacher, Mrs. Milano, scolded me for "being a nuisance and disrupting her lesson." I tried to remain unnoticed during the rest of class — not moving even an inch for fear that my actions would cause yet another bad event to come my way.

8 It was after English class that I noticed a person who was having an even worse day than I was.

9 Little Ferguson Amey, the smartest kid in the entire sixth grade, was getting picked on as usual. Ferguson stood tall, seemingly unphased by the taunts of the older boys, but I could see the angry tears beginning to swell up in his eyes. Just then something snapped in me. I was having a horrible day out of shear bad luck, but Ferguson was having a bad day because of these mean older boys. I stood tall like Ferguson and walked over to the taunting boys.

10 "You're not impressing anyone by making Ferguson feel bad. I know Ferguson is very smart, but that's no excuse for you to try to make him upset," I said.

11 Ferguson's eyes lit up and I received a punch to the nose.

12 Teachers, who had watched the entire scene, quickly sent the older boys to the principal's office.

13 Ferguson got a big wad of toilet paper to hold on my bleeding nose. He told me he thought it was really "cool" that I stood up for him — no one had ever had the courage to stand up for him before. I told him I thought he was really "cool" too, because he was strong enough to endure all that teasing without getting into fights all the time. He really appreciated that comment.

14 So, that's how I met my best friend. Ferguson was a friend who would stick by my side through middle school, high school, and probably the rest of my life. And I am sure I wouldn't have met him if it were not for that amazing, dreadful, horrible day.

Go On

21. What is the author's purpose for writing this passage?

A. to persuade the reader not to fight

X B. to teach the reader to stand up for others

C. to describe a bad day

D. to inform the reader about Ferguson's life

22. What is the main message of the passage?

A. You can make a bad day better by finding someone whose having an even worse day.

X B. If you do a good deed, then happiness will find its way back to you.

C. If you do a good deed, you will be punished.

D. You should not stand up for other people because you will only get hurt.

Go On

23. In your own words, explain the connection between the horrible part of the narrator's day and the amazing part of his day.

Support your answer with **two** details from the passage.

Short-answer responses may vary. Because the narrator was having such a bad day himself, he had a newfound sympathy for Ferguson Amey, who was being teased by mean, older boys. The author stood up for Ferguson and, as a result, the two boys became best friends.

24. Read this sentence from the fifth paragraph of the passage.

"I was *mortified*, but I tried to prove to Sabrina that it didn't bother me, and I pretended to laugh at myself."

The word *mortified* in the sentence above means–

A. amused.

B. confused.

X **C.** embarrassed.

D. angry.

25. When the narrator is punched in the nose, the setting is probably–

A. in another classroom.

B. in the lunch line.

C. in English class.

X **D.** in the hallway.

Go On

Read this selection. Then answer the questions that follow.

Storm Chasers

1 Many people fear "Mother Nature" and the unpredictable weather she has been known to cause, but there are those who are fascinated by her. They want to see her effects up close. As a matter of fact, they go out looking for bad weather and storms. These people are known as the storm chasers.

2 Storm chasers are everyday people who are awestruck by severe storms and extreme weather. They actually go out in search of it! They sometimes travel hundreds of miles from state to state in search of the big storm. Certain areas of the United States, including the Great Plains and the Midwest, are known to produce such storms. As a result, many of the chasers come from those areas or settle there.

3 Usually, the main goal of the storm chaser is to witness a tornado, but this isn't always the case. Oftentimes, the severe weather becomes dangerous. The storm chasers could be risking their own safety if they continue to chase the storm. When the risk is too great, storm chasers have to give up the chase. For most, however, the real reward is the total experience of the storm itself and getting to see nature's awesome power up close.

4 Technological advances have given meteorologists, scientists who study weather, the ability to predict certain weather patterns and storms. Meteorologists are people who have earned a special degree from a university and who work to forecast and report the weather.

5 Today, storm chasers have many more tools and information to work with than the first chasers did. Using this information, storm chasers are likely to experience more storms than ever before. While most storm chasers are there for the experience and to take photographs or to shoot video, some do collect meteorological information for weather research.

6 Storm chasers come from all walks of life, but their interest in weather and storms gives them something in common. As long as there is weather to observe, storm chasers will continue to follow the skies.

Go On

Meeting of the Future Storm Chasers Club

1 Good afternoon, fellow students and future storm chasers. As this club's founder and president, I would like to welcome you to the first meeting of the Future Storm Chasers Club. I hope we can convince many more storm chasers to join us in the future!

2 Although we are too young to be storm chasers, it is not too soon to begin preparing for this thrilling hobby. In the meetings of this club, we will talk about the different things storm chasers do. We have lined up some storm chasers as guest speakers. They will not only describe what they do as storm chasers, they will show pictures and video they have taken while out chasing storms. The images are really neat. I've met with some of these people, and they know a lot about storm chasing.

3 Another part of storm chasing we will talk about is safety. Storm chasing is an extremely dangerous activity, and it is very important to understand how to stay safe. We want to live to tell others what we have seen. Storm chasers often get much closer to tornadoes and other forms of severe weather than most people would choose to, so they have to know how to handle dangerous situations. Some of our speakers will be covering this issue in their presentations, so you should pay close attention.

4 Our speaker next week will be Jim Jeffries, a storm chaser who has followed tornadoes all over the Midwest. Jeffries has been chasing storms for over 10 years. He likes the activity so much, he's gotten his wife and brother involved in storm chasing. Together, they have chased hundreds of storms. He knows so much about this topic, that you'll be amazed at the information he will be able to share. Plus, he has great safety tips that we should really pay attention to. Anyone who would like to hear his fascinating speech should be here at 3:00 p.m. next Wednesday. Tell your friends and family. Everyone is welcome.

5 Thank you all for coming to this meeting. I hope to see everyone next week. Don't forget to spread the word. We want all future storm chasers to join the club!

Go On

26. Which of the following BEST describes the author's purpose?
    - **A.** to discuss the differences between people who fear storms and storm chasers
    - **B.** to explain why storm chasing is easier today than ever before
    - X **C.** to describe why and how some people chase storms
    - **D.** to describe severe storms and tornados

27. Meteorologists and storm chasers are similar because–
    - **A.** they both receive degrees from universities.
    - X **B.** they both are interested in weather.
    - **C.** they both travel to find storms.
    - **D.** they both are from the Midwest.

28. What causes storm chasers to seek out severe weather?
    - **A.** They are paid by the government to do weather research.
    - **B.** Meteorologists ask the storm chasers to do weather research.
    - **C.** Storm chasers want to obtain storm-chasing licenses.
    - X **D.** Storm chasers are fascinated by severe weather and want to experience it firsthand.

29. What is the main idea of the speech, "Meeting of the Future Storm Chasers Club"?
    - **A.** A student is trying to increase the membership of the Future Storm Chasers Club.
    - **B.** A student is giving information about the guest speaker for the Future Storm Chasers Club meeting.
    - X **C.** A student is explaining why the Future Storm Chasers Club has been founded and its purpose.
    - **D.** A student is explaining the dangers of storm chasing to members of the Future Storm Chasers Club.

Go On

30. Which of the following sentences from "Meeting of the Future Storm Chasers Club" is a fact?

X**A.** "In the meetings of this club, we will talk about the different things storm chasers do."

B. "Some of our speakers will be covering this issue in their presentations, so you should pay close attention."

C. "Although we are too young to be storm chasers, it is not too soon to begin preparing for this thrilling hobby."

D. "Anyone who would like to hear his fascinating speech should be here at 3:00 p.m. next Wednesday."

31. "Storm Chasers" differs from "Meeting of the Future Storm Chasers Club" because "Storm Chasers" focuses more on–

A. what the club will do during its meetings.

B. what storm chasers talk about in their speeches.

X**C.** what storm chasers do and what tools they use.

D. how old someone must be to become a storm chaser.

Go On

Read this selection. Then answer the questions that follow.

Sail Away

1 It was a beautiful day. The temperature was not too hot and not too cool; it felt just right. The deep blue sky was filled with puffy white clouds. The wind was perfect for sailing. Chris enjoyed the feeling of the cool wind and the warm sun.

2 Chris' friend Matt had decided to test out his sea legs for the first time. Matt had never been on a sailboat, so Chris was hoping to teach him how the sails worked. Chris had been sailing for years; his father had taught him many things. Chris was happy to share what he knew with his friend, but there was something he wanted Matt to know before moving on to any other topic. Chris' first rule was important to him: Matt had to wear a life jacket.

3 "I don't need a life jacket. I'm a good swimmer," Matt told Chris. But Chris insisted they both had to wear the bright orange protective vests. Chris wouldn't leave the dock until Matt had snapped the life jacket around him.

4 "I feel silly wearing this thing," Matt complained as they headed out. "People will think I'm a baby if they see me with this on. I cannot believe you are not embarrassed to be seen in this stupid-looking thing."

5 "I'm not, and you shouldn't be either. Quit complaining and help me with the mainsail," Chris replied. "Loosen the rope, but don't let go until I tell you." Chris simply pretended that Matt was not complaining and he focused on sailing.

6 Matt did as he was told. "Chris is pretty bossy out here," he thought to himself. "He doesn't act like this on land. There must be something in the water that makes him act a little weird." Rather than argue, Matt decided to take in the sights. He was quickly preoccupied with a group of pelicans flying over the boat. He turned his head as a pelican swooped down to the water to get a fish. He was amazed by the bird. He focused only on what it was doing. Instead of paying attention to his grip on the line, he continued to stare at the bird. Suddenly, the line went flying into the air. The wind caught the mainsail and sent the boom flying around to where Matt was standing. Bam! The boom hit Matt in the upper part of his arm, just below his shoulder. It was a solid hit, which Matt was not expecting. He was knocked off the side of the boat as the sail and the boom seemed to come alive.

Go On

7 Chris saw what had happened and quickly went into action. He grabbed a small round float and threw it toward Matt. The float had a long rope that Chris tied to the side of the boat. Matt was bobbing in the water; his life jacket kept him afloat. Chris wrestled the sail's line back onto its cleat to stop the boom from moving back and forth across the boat. Then he went to check on Matt again. He yelled to Matt, "Are you OK?"

8 "I think so. But the water is freezing!" Matt clung tightly to the round float. He couldn't believe how fast everything had happened. He couldn't believe he was now in the water.

9 "Try to swim. I'll pull." Chris used every muscle he had to pull Matt and the float closer to the boat. Matt could only kick his legs. His arms grappled with the float, tugging on it with all his might.

10 Matt got to the boat, and Chris helped him up to the deck. Matt wrapped himself in a towel. The cool wind made him shiver. "What happened?"

11 "You were hit by the boom. I think you must have let go of the line and the wind caught the sail. All I saw were your feet flying over the side. Are you OK?"

12 Matt could hear the concern in Chris' voice. He wanted his friend to know he was OK, just a little shaken from the shock of being tossed overboard. "Yeah I'm fine, but I'm going to have a wonderful bruise on my arm. And I promise I'll never whine at you again about wearing a silly life jacket."

Go On

32. What caused Matt to let go of the rope?

A. Chris told him to let go.

B. Matt wasn't strong enough to hold the rope.

C. A pelican swooped down and bit him.

X**D.** He was watching the pelicans and didn't hold the rope tightly.

33. At the beginning of the passage, Matt stops arguing with Chris and puts on a life jacket because–

A. Matt realizes that Chris is right.

X**B.** Matt would rather enjoy the scenery than argue with Chris.

C. Matt doesn't know enough about sailing to argue with Chris.

D. Matt is too busy learning how the sails work.

34. The tone of the sixth paragraph can best be described as–

A. gloomy

B. tender

C. solemn

X**D.** exciting

Go On

Read this selection. Then answer the questions that follow.

Camp Abbenaki

1 Andres gazed out the bus window at trees as they whirled by his view. He and 15 boys his age traveled down a bumpy country road leading to Camp Abbenaki. It was Andres' first time staying away from home alone.

2 He looked at the unfamiliar faces of the other boys on the bus. Some boys came with a friend and they were chatting quietly in their seats, but most looked just as nervous as Andres felt about leaving his home and going to an unfamiliar place with a bunch of unfamiliar people.

3 Camp Abbenaki was one of the most fun summer camps for boys in the United States—so the pamphlet said. Andres poured over Camp Abbenaki's pamphlet when he received it. It described fields of sports facilities, a rock climbing wall, and a mile-long beach with a zip-line you could ride from its 50-foot perch down into the water. There were group activities every day and plenty of free time to play a soccer game or just relax under a tree.

4 Andres got excited thinking about everything he would get to do at camp this summer. He knew he was going to have to be brave these first few days. He needed to make new friends and learn to take care of himself; his friends and family at home wouldn't be here to help him along the way.

5 "I'm not a little kid anymore anyway," Andres thought. "I should be able to do things on my own."

6 Andres felt a wave of fear wash over him. What if he couldn't learn to live on his own? What if he couldn't make friends? What if he couldn't live so far away from his family? What if he missed his friends and family so much that he couldn't bear it?

7 Andres took three deep breaths. He saw the Camp Abbenaki sign go by the bus window. In just a few minutes, Andres would be unloading his luggage and meeting his new camp counselors and cabin mates.

8 Andres had a tough choice to make. How would he cope with this situation? He had arrived at camp and it was time to take action.

Go On

9 "I can't be shy," Andres decided. "I can't give up. I've got to be brave…or else I'll just be acting like a little kid again and I don't want to be a little kid anymore."

10 Andres smiled at the boy sitting across from him on the bus. The boy smiled back.

11 "Hi, my name is Andres."

12 "Hi, my name's Ryan," the boy answered. "It's nice to meet you. Are you excited to be at camp this summer?"

13 "Yes, I can't wait!" Andres answered.

Go On

35. The passage, Camp Abbenaki, is told in–

A. first person.

B. objective.

C. third person omniscient.

X**D.** third person limited omniscient.

36. What is the author's purpose for writing the passage "Camp Abbenaki"?

A. to argue that young people are not ready emotionally to go away to camp

B. to inform the reader about the facilities at Camp Abbenaki

C. to explain how to resolve problems and calm fears

X**D.** to describe a boy's journey to camp and his fears about growing up

Go On

37. What is the main message in the story "Camp Abbenaki"?

A. Going away to camp for the first time is a frightening experience.

B. Young people are shy when they find themselves in a new situation.

C. Young people shouldn't go to camp because it will make them feel nervous.

X**D.** To grow up, young people must adjust to new situations and learn to be independent.

38. Why does Andres begin to fear going to camp during the bus ride?

A. He overhears a story about a camper who was lost the previous summer.

B. He looks out the bus window and sees the sign for the camp.

X**C.** He thinks about how he is not a little kid anymore and he will have to do things on his own now.

D. He decides that he will be brave; he won't be shy, and he won't give up.

Go On

39. Which of these sentences best summarizes the passage?

X A. Andres is nervous about going away to camp, but decides to try to make friends and have fun.

B. Andres goes to Camp Abbenaki, which features a rock climbing wall and a mile-long beach.

C. Andres makes a new friend on his way to Camp Abbenaki.

D. Andres is nervous about going away to camp for the first time, but so are some of the other boys on the bus.

40. Which of the following words describes Andres' mood at the end of the passage?

A. resigned

B. nervous

X C. determined

D. indifferent

STOP

1 Ⓐ ● Ⓒ Ⓓ

2 ● Ⓑ Ⓒ Ⓓ

3 ● Ⓑ Ⓒ Ⓓ

4 Ⓐ Ⓑ Ⓒ ●

5 Ⓐ ● Ⓒ Ⓓ

6

Short-answer responses may vary. The poet dreams of going back to being a swinger of birches whenever he is "weary of considerations." He sees swinging on birch trees as a temporary escape from the cares of the world.

7 Ⓐ Ⓑ ● Ⓓ

8 Ⓐ ● Ⓒ Ⓓ

9 Ⓐ Ⓑ Ⓒ ●

© Englefield & Associates, Inc.

10

Extended-response answers may vary. The author wrote this selection to give information about Cozumel in the past and present. The first part of the selection describes the present-day highlights of Cozumel. It is a popular tourist destination, attracting many people from all over the world to its beaches. People can snorkel and enjoy other water sports while on vacation. They can also walk on nature trails or go shopping. The author also explains about the history of the island in the second part of the selection. It used to be a pilgrimage site and a center of Mayan trading. The island was once mainly occupied by pirates, and then was taken over by Spanish settlers. After much of the population died from a smallpox epidemic, the island eventually grew into a popular place for tourists.

11 Ⓐ Ⓑ Ⓒ ●

12 Ⓐ Ⓑ Ⓒ ●

13 ● Ⓑ Ⓒ Ⓓ

14 Ⓐ Ⓑ ● Ⓓ

15 Ⓐ ● Ⓒ Ⓓ

16 Ⓐ Ⓑ Ⓒ ●

17 Ⓐ Ⓑ ● Ⓓ

Copying is Prohibited
© Englefield & Associates, Inc.

18 Ⓐ Ⓑ Ⓒ ●

19 Ⓐ Ⓑ ● Ⓓ

20 Ⓐ Ⓑ ● Ⓓ

21 Ⓐ ● Ⓒ Ⓓ

22 Ⓐ ● Ⓒ Ⓓ

23

Short-answer responses may vary. Because the narrator was having such a bad day himself, he had a newfound sympathy for Ferguson Amey, who was being teased by mean, older boys. The author stood up for Ferguson and, as a result, the two boys became best friends.

24 Ⓐ Ⓑ ● Ⓓ

25 Ⓐ Ⓑ Ⓒ ●

26 Ⓐ Ⓑ ● Ⓓ

27 Ⓐ ● Ⓒ Ⓓ

28 Ⓐ Ⓑ Ⓒ ●

29 Ⓐ Ⓑ ● Ⓓ

30 ● Ⓑ Ⓒ Ⓓ

31 Ⓐ Ⓑ ● Ⓓ

32 Ⓐ Ⓑ Ⓒ ●

33 Ⓐ ● Ⓒ Ⓓ

34 Ⓐ Ⓑ Ⓒ ●

35 Ⓐ Ⓑ Ⓒ ●

36 Ⓐ Ⓑ Ⓒ ●

37 Ⓐ Ⓑ Ⓒ ●

38 Ⓐ Ⓑ ● Ⓓ

39 ● Ⓑ Ⓒ Ⓓ

40 Ⓐ Ⓑ ● Ⓓ

Copying is Prohibited
© Englefield & Associates, Inc.

Question	Standard	Answer	Keywords
1	RL.6.2	B	Theme
2	RL.6.10	A	Plot
3	RL.6.5	A	Development of Theme
4	RL.6.10	D	Main Idea
5	RL.6.4	B	Understanding Literary Devices
6	RL.6.1	—	Main Idea
7	RI.6.9	C	Find Similarities and Differences Across Texts
8	RI.6.9	B	Find Similarities and Differences Across Texts
9	RI.6.10	D	Comprehension
10	RI.6.6	—	Author's Purpose
11	RI.6.4	D	Word Definition
12	RL.6.6	D	Point of View
13	RL.6.4	A	Mood, Theme
14	RL.6.2	C	Summarize
15	RL.6.5	B	Analyze Setting
16	RI.6.2	D	Summarize
17	RI.6.4	C	Connotative Meaning
18	RI.6.10	D	Compare and Contrast
19	RI.6.1	C	Make Connections
20	RI.6.3	C	Analyze How Authors Organize Information

—see analysis for constructed response

Question	Standard	Answer	Keywords
21	RL.6.10	B	Author's Purpose
22	RL.6.2	B	Main Idea
23	RL.6.2	—	Summarize
24	RL.6.4	C	Use Context Clues
25	RL.6.10	D	Plot
26	RI.6.6	C	Author's Purpose
27	RI.6.10	B	Compare and Contrast
28	RI.6.1	D	Use Text Structure to Locate Information
29	RI.6.2	C	Central Idea
30	RI.6.8	A	Distinguish Fact from Opinion
31	RI.6.9	C	Compare Communication in Different Forms
32	RL.6.3	D	Cause and Effect
33	RL.6.1	B	Locate Information
34	RL.6.5	D	Recognize How Tone Affects a Text
35	RL.6.6	D	Point of View
36	RL.6.10	D	Author's Purpose
37	RL.6.2	D	Theme
38	RL.6.10	C	Plot
39	RL.6.2	A	Summarize
40	RL.6.3	C	Identify Characters

—*see analysis for constructed response*

Copying is Prohibited
© Englefield & Associates, Inc.

Reading Assessment One: Correlation Chart

Use this chart to identify areas for improvement for individual students or for the class as a whole. For example, enter students' names in the left-hand column. When a student misses a question, place an "X" in the corresponding box. A column with a large number of "Xs" shows that the class needs more practice with that particular objective.

Correlation	RL.6.2	RL.6.10	RL.6.5	RL.6.10	RL.6.4	RL.6.1	RI.6.9	RI.6.9	RI.6.10	RI.6.6	RL.6.4	RL.6.6	RL.6.4	RL.6.2	RL.6.5	RI.6.2	RI.6.4	RI.6.10	RI.6.1	RI.6.3
Answer	B	A	A	D	B	—	C	B	D	—	D	D	A	C	B	D	C	D	C	C
Question	1	2	3	4	5	6	7	8	9	10	11	12	13	14	15	16	17	18	19	20
Student Names																				

—see analysis for constructed response

© Englefield & Associates, Inc.

Question	21	22	23	24	25	26	27	28	29	30	31	32	33	34	35	36	37	38	39	40
Correlation	RL.6.10	RL.6.2	RL.6.2	RL.6.4	RL.6.10	RI.6.6	RI.6.10	RI.6.1	RI.6.2	RI.6.8	RI.6.9	RL.6.3	RL.6.1	RL.6.5	RL.6.6	RL.6.10	RL.6.2	RL.6.10	RL.6.2	RL.6.3
Answer	B	B	—	C	D	C	B	D	C	A	C	D	B	D	D	D	D	C	A	C
Student Names																				

—see analysis for constructed response

Copying is Prohibited
© Englefield & Associates, Inc.

Reading Assessment Two

Responses *Throughout this section, pages from Reading Assessment Two of the Student Workbook are included in reduced-page format. Correct multiple-choice answers and sample responses for each constructed-response item are indicated.*

Directions:

This Grade 6 Reading Assessment has multiple-choice and short-answer questions.

There are several important things to remember as you take this test:

- Read each multiple-choice question carefully. Think about what is being asked. Then fill in one answer bubble to mark your answer.
- If you do not know the answer to a multiple-choice question, skip it and go on. If you have time, go back to the questions you skipped and answer them.
- For short-answer questions, write your response clearly and neatly in the box provided.
- If you finish the Assessment early, go back and check over your work.

Reading Assessment Two

Directions for Taking the Reading Assessment

The Reading Assessment contains six reading selections and 40 questions. Some of the selections are fiction, while others are nonfiction. Read each selection and the questions that follow carefully. You may look back at any selection as many times as you would like. If you are unsure of a question, you can move to the next question and go back to the question you skipped later.

Multiple-choice questions require you to pick the best answer out of four possible choices. Only one answer is correct. The short-answer questions will ask you to write your answer and explain your thinking using words. Remember to read the questions and the answer choices carefully. You will mark your answers on the answer document.

When you finish, check your answers.

Read this selection. Then answer the questions that follow.

Mayor Bass Announces Megamart Construction

by Adella Estado
Sunshine Press Reporter

1 FLORIDA—Mixed reactions filled the air in City Hall Wednesday morning as Mayor Ric Bass announced construction plans for a Megamart on Route 16 near the Sakota River.

2 The City Hall crowd seemed split in spirit. While some residents rejoiced at the news, others jumped out of their chairs outraged. One resident, Mike Giordano of Route 16, was so startled by the news that he leapt from his seat knocking over his chair and the other five chairs in front of him—creating a domino-like effect.

3 Marge Cunningham, 76, of 125 Oak Wood St. broke a finger and sustained minor bruises after the man sitting behind her fell forward pushing her and her chair to the floor.

4 After about ten minutes of public outcry, for and against the Megamart, Mayor Bass was able to calm the crowd to a silence.

5 "We, your city officials, believe Megamart will be a beneficial addition to our town," Bass said. "We understand your concern as Megamart has gained the infamous reputation for closing small local businesses wherever it goes; however, we believe the benefits will outweigh any disadvantage the store may create for our local businesses."

6 The mayor said the new store will create more than 100 new jobs between its construction crew and its full-time employees. The store will sell everything from kitchen appliances to clothing for the entire family. Megamart will also sell a variety of food brands and fresh fruit from around the world.

7 "Our town doesn't have many shopping options, so I usually travel to Richland, 30 miles away, when I need to buy anything," Julie Simmons said. "Megamart will be so nice to have just down the street. I will have so many more brands to choose from at much lower prices than any of the local stores can offer."

8 The mayor said Megamart construction will begin this April and the store should be open by November. He will have an open discussion Tuesday, Feb. 25 at 8 p.m. in City Hall to address any concerns residents may have about the new Megamart store.

Go On

Letters to the Editor
Megamart Will Make Local Stores Depart

1 Dear Editor,

2 I am writing to address the opposing side of the Megamart issue because I believe it was not adequately covered in yesterday's article, "Mayor Bass announces Megamart construction."

3 I am incredibly concerned about our town's situation at hand. Our town boasts 15 successful, small locally-owned businesses. Of these businesses, seven have been in our town for more than 50 years.

4 I am the owner of the oldest locally-owned business in our town: The J. R. & P. Drugstore. My great-grandparents built the drugstore in 1917 when the town's population was only 400. The J. R. & P. Drugstore has seen this town grow and change for almost a century now, but I fear it will not survive long enough to celebrate its centennial birthday.

5 The mayor admitted that Megamart is infamous for closing small businesses wherever it goes and that is exactly what will happen to our 15 small locally-owned businesses.

6 Megamart will create new jobs, but it will also take away jobs as it closes small businesses owned by local people. Local entrepreneurs cannot compete with the low prices of Megamart, and they will have to move their stores elsewhere to keep their sales up and their businesses running.

7 I ask all residents to attend the mayor's open discussion in City Hall Tuesday, Feb. 25, at 8 p.m. so we all are aware of the concerns our community has about the construction of Megamart.

8 Sincerely,
Lucidia James Pickett
Owner of J. R. & P. Drugstore

Go On

1. Which sentence from the newspaper articles is an example of the author using persuasion with the reading audience?

   A. "The J. R. & P. Drugstore has seen this town grow and change for almost a century now, but I fear it will not survive long enough to celebrate its centennial birthday."

   B. "The mayor said the new store will create more than 100 new jobs between its construction crew and its full time employees."

   X **C.** "I ask all residents to attend the mayor's open discussion in City Hall Tuesday, Feb. 25, at 8 p.m. so we all are aware of the concerns our community has about the construction of Megamart."

   D. "The mayor said Megamart construction will begin this April and the store should be open by November."

2. Lucidia wrote a Letter to the Editor because–

   X **A.** she is concerned for the small local businesses and thinks the newspaper article did not adequately cover the opposing side of the issue.

   B. she owns a small business and Megamart is making her sales decrease.

   C. she lives on Route 16 and she is concerned there will be a dangerous increase of traffic on her road.

   D. she had to drive to Richland, 30 miles away, to buy products, but now Megamart will be just down the road and its location will be convenient for her.

Go On

3. Which of the following arguments does Ms. Pickett make in response to statements made in favor of the new Megamart?

   A. Some of the new jobs created by Megamart will be temporary.

   B. Local businesses offer better products than Megamart.

   X **C.** Jobs will be lost as well as gained, since local businesses will be forced to move away or close.

   D. Local businesses can offer prices that are competitive with those of Megamart.

4. Which of the following BEST summarizes the article "Mayor Bass Announces Megamart Construction"?

   A. It is being debated whether or not Megamart hurts local businesses.

   B. Megamart supporters argue that the new Megamart will provide better service to shoppers.

   C. Local citizens are deeply divided over the Megamart issue.

   X **D.** Citizens' reactions were mixed when the mayor announced construction plans for a new Megamart store.

Go On

5. Which of the following statements is true?

   A. The mayor thinks the new Megamart will help local businesses.

   X B. The mayor believes the advantages of the new Megamart will outweigh the disadvantages.

   C. The mayor is opposed to the new Megamart.

   D. The mayor will make up his mind about the new Megamart after the open discussion on February 25.

6. How is the mayor's opinion of Megamart different from Lucidia's opinion of Megamart?

   A. The mayor believes Megamart will create new jobs and Lucidia believes Megamart will not create new jobs.

   X B. The mayor believes Megamart will benefit the town and Lucidia believes Megamart will hurt the town by closing local businesses.

   C. The mayor believes Megamart will give shoppers more variety and Lucidia believes Megamart will make customers pay too much for their products.

   D. The mayor believes Megamart will make customers pay too much for their products and Lucidia believes Megamart will benefit the town.

Go On

7. Does Sunshine Press reporter Adella Estado give equal attention to both sides in the Megamart debate?

   Support your answer with **four** details from the article.

Extended-response answers may vary. The article conveys the depth of the controversy surrounding the construction of a new Megamart by describing the extreme reactions of the citizens following the mayor's announcement. However, the article does not give equal space to the both sides in the debate. The article quotes both the mayor and resident Julie Simmons, who list numerous arguments in favor of building the Megamart. The only argument against Megamart is presented by the mayor, who is pro-Megamart. He admits that Megamart has the "reputation for closing small local businesses wherever it goes," but he continues by saying that the benefits of building a new Megamart will outweigh the disadvantages. The article does not quote anyone who is against the new Megamart.

8. Read this sentence from the fifth paragraph of the Letter to the Editor "Megamart Will Make Local Stores Depart."

   "The mayor admitted that Megamart is *infamous* for closing small businesses wherever it goes, and that is exactly what will happen to our fifteen small, locally-owned businesses."

   The word *infamous* means–

   A. is not famous for.

   B. is unfairly accused of.

   X C. has a bad reputation for.

   D. is not known for.

9. Which of the following statements is true of both articles "Mayor Bass Announces Megamart Construction" and "Megamart Will Make Local Stores Depart"?

   A. The author's purpose is to persuade the reader.

   B. Both are written in the first person.

   C. The author should present both sides in a debate.

   X D. Both are examples of nonfiction.

10. You are writing a report about the benefits of Megamart. Which of the following points would you **not** include in your report?

   A. Megamart offers customers low prices.

   B. Megamart offers customers variety in product brands.

   C. Megamart sells everything from kitchen appliances to clothes for the whole family.

   X D. Megamart closes similar businesses that cannot compete with Megamart's low prices.

Go On

Read this selection. Then answer the questions that follow.

Travel south? Why? Look at all the beautiful snow!

By Sheryl Cooper

1 Every year during December, I am guaranteed to hear the same question: "Are you going to travel south this month?" It drives me crazy! I live in northern Minnesota for a reason. I love the winter.

2 Winter is my favorite season. I know that I may be part of a minority, but I think that people should give winter a fighting chance. The temperatures are freezing, but who doesn't like to come home to a warm house, or wear large soft sweaters everyday, or curl up next to a warm fire with a tall glass of hot chocolate?

3 There are also many activities to do outside when it's cold. There's skiing, snow boarding, ice skating, snow mobiling, ice fishing, hunting, snowman building, snowball fighting, and snow angel making, just to name a few. There are also many indoor activities that can be pursued while staying out of the cold weather. There's not a moment of boredom in the month of December so I don't understand why people leave for warmer climates. They are missing the simple pleasures of the snow that are waiting for them at home.

4 Snow—this is by far the greatest reason why I love the winter so much. When the snow falls, it looks like a whimsical ballet of little white ballerinas floating in the air. It's a magical experience to find yourself caught in a snowfall. It's like someone is shaking up your life's snow globe and you get to experience the magic from the inside. Then after the snowfall, the snow covers everything and makes it sparkle with white and silver diamond radiance.

5 I believe that everyone should experience a northern winter and be excited to do so. It's a magical season full of warmth and love despite the cold temperatures outside. People in northern Minnesota should not be traveling south to warmer weather; the people living in the warmer weather should travel to Minnesota and experience a real winter in all its radiance.

Go On

I'm traveling south the second it snows!

By Trevor Wallenski

1 I live in Boston, Massachusetts. I love Boston. I love the summer months when the weather is warm, but not too hot. I love the history in Boston. The one and only thing that I don't like in Boston is the snow, and I plan on taking a long vacation down south once it comes.

2 I wouldn't want to be anywhere else but in Boston during the rest of the year; however, when those icy flakes start falling my love turns to disgust. How could anyone love the frigid temperatures that chill you to the bone or enjoy the precariously icy walkways or the slushy, slippery roads? Everything is colder and more dangerous during the winter time. It is not a happy season. It is a season of cold and despair.

3 During the winter, a person's immune system will weaken and he or she will become prone to many more bouts of the cold or flu than during the other seasons of the year.

4 Tissues need to be at hand at all times since the cold weather turns runny noses into the norm.

5 The days are dark and gloomy. Because of the time change, it is dark for more hours during the day in the winter, but down south it is still sunny and warm. Personally, I feel happier when I see more sunlight during each day. I also believe that I eat healthier, drink more water, and generally feel better in warmer weather. Most people will agree when I say that winter is the worst of the seasons and that a nice warm vacation is needed when the snow begins to fall.

Go On

11. In Sheryl's selection, what does she describe as being "full of warmth and love despite the cold temperatures"?

 A. the snow
 X B. the winter
 C. a sleigh ride
 D. a house

12. What does Trevor's and Sheryl's titles tell you about their points of view on winter?

 A. Sheryl's title tells the reader that she likes the seasons; Trevor's title tells the reader that he dislikes the seasons.
 X B. Sheryl's title tells the reader that she likes snow; Trevor's title tells the reader that he plans to travel south once the snow begins to fall.
 C. Sheryl's title tells the reader that she likes to ice skate; Trevor's title tells the reader that he likes to surf.
 D. Sheryl's title tells the reader that she does not like the winter; Trevor's title tells the reader that he does like the winter.

Go On

13. Evaluate each author's argument about winter. Which author makes the better argument?

 Use **two** examples from the text to support your answer.

Short-answer responses may vary. I think that Trevor makes a stronger argument about winter because he states more examples of why people should dislike winter than Sheryl's passage states about why people should like winter. Trevor says that most people believe his argument, so that probably means that it is a strong one. I agree with Trevor when he says that the winter is dark and gloomy because it's dark outside more often and everything is cold—too cold.

14. How does Trevor describe walkways during the winter?

 A. He says they are covered in salt that gets on your shoes and clothes.
 B. He says they are beautiful when they are covered with snow.
 C. He says they are slushy and slippery.
 X D. He says they are precariously icy.

15. What is each author's purpose for writing his or her selection?

 X A. Both authors persuade the reader to either like or to dislike winter.
 B. Sheryl's selection is persuasive; Trevor's selection is narrative.
 C. Sheryl's selection is poetic; Trevor's selection is expository.
 D. Both authors' wrote narrative selections.

Go On

Read this selection. Then answer the questions that follow.

The New Scooter

1 A.J. tugged at the wrapping paper. Each tear revealed more of what he had hoped to see. Slowly, a brand new scooter made its way out of the box. A fresh-cut piece of chocolate cake sat untouched on the table. All A.J. could think about was trying out his new scooter. The raindrops tapping against the windowpane told him his first adventure would have to wait for another day.

2 The scooter may have been a birthday gift, but to A.J. it was much more than that. A.J. had asked for the same scooter for his last birthday; he had not gotten it. Instead, he had gotten some clothes and a speech from his parents about how important it was to do well in school. For the next year, A.J. worked as hard as he could in every class. He made the honor roll every quarter. A.J. looked at the scooter and smiled. To him, it stood for all the homework he had worked so hard on.

3 Another stormy day passed before A.J. saw light break through the dark clouds. The shiny scooter rested against the sun-porch railing. The fluorescent green wheels popped with color. The metallic shaft and handlebars glimmered in the light. A.J. grabbed his new toy and pushed both himself and the scooter outside with excitement. With one foot on the scooter's base, he used his other leg to give the scooter a gentle push. He then lifted his other leg to the scooter base and drifted down his driveway. There were several other kids outside enjoying the sun. It wasn't long before A.J. saw an old friend.

4 "Hey, Ann!" A.J. cried out. "What do you think of my new scooter?" He hardly gave her enough time to answer. He spun the scooter around on its front wheel, and he was off in another direction.

5 When Ann was able to get close to the duo, she admired A.J.'s new set of wheels. She had seen a scooter just like it at the bike shop, but the one she wanted had purple wheels. Ann watched as A.J. raced up and down the concrete driveway. It was as if he had been riding all his life.

6 "You're pretty good at making that thing move," she said as he whizzed past her for the second time. A.J. stopped in front of Ann and decided this was the perfect opportunity to impress her with some tricks.

7 "Watch this!" A.J. said while he rode the scooter with just one hand. The more he rode, the braver he became. Holding onto the handlebars tightly, he made the scooter hop. Next, he lifted his right leg forward; then, he swung it behind him. He steered the scooter to the right and to the left, all while balancing on one leg. A.J. hardly let the scooter lose momentum before he would propel it forward again.

Go On

8 "Please be careful! You should be wearing a helmet if you're going to do tricks like that," Ann reminded him, but he didn't seem to pay attention to her.

9 It wasn't until A.J. felt like increasing the difficulty of his stunts that he actually let go of the scooter. He dropped it in the grass when he found some wooden boards lying by the side of the garage. He arranged them carefully until they formed a small ramp like the one he had seen in the bicycle magazines he kept in his room. "I'm ready for some action now," A.J. cried out, hoping Ann was watching him.

10 The first time over the ramp seemed easy, and A.J.'s confidence grew. "That was great!" Ann said, smiling.

11 She didn't want to admit it, but she hoped he would ask her if she wanted to ride his scooter. She wanted to try a trick or two, but A.J. wouldn't let go of his new scooter.

12 He wheeled the scooter around for his second attempt. "This one will be even better," he shouted.

13 A.J. zipped up and down the drive and made his way toward the ramp. Just as the front wheel reached the board, the scooter flipped, leaving A.J. on the hard pavement. Ann rushed over and saw that A.J. had some scrapes and a large knot on his forehead. "Are you OK?" she said.

14 A.J. sat up slowly, rubbing his head. "On a scale of one to ten, what would you give me for that stunt?" asked A.J. It was his way of saying, "I'm fine." They both started laughing.

15 "I'll give you a ten if you promise not to do that again until you've got a helmet."

16 "It's a deal," said A.J. He climbed to his feet and looked around for the misplaced scooter. Upon careful examination, nothing seemed to be out of place. Although he knew he needed to take a break from the scooter, A.J. couldn't wait to try it again!

Go On

16. Which of the following words offers the BEST description of A.J.?

A. boring

B. scared

C. lonely

X **D.** adventurous

17. In the eighth paragraph of the story, why does the author include foreshadowing?

A. to let the reader know that Ann was not concerned about A.J.'s safety

X **B.** to let the reader know that Ann was worried about A.J.'s safety

C. to let the reader know that A.J. was not concerned about his safety

D. to let the reader know that A.J. was worried about his safety

Go On

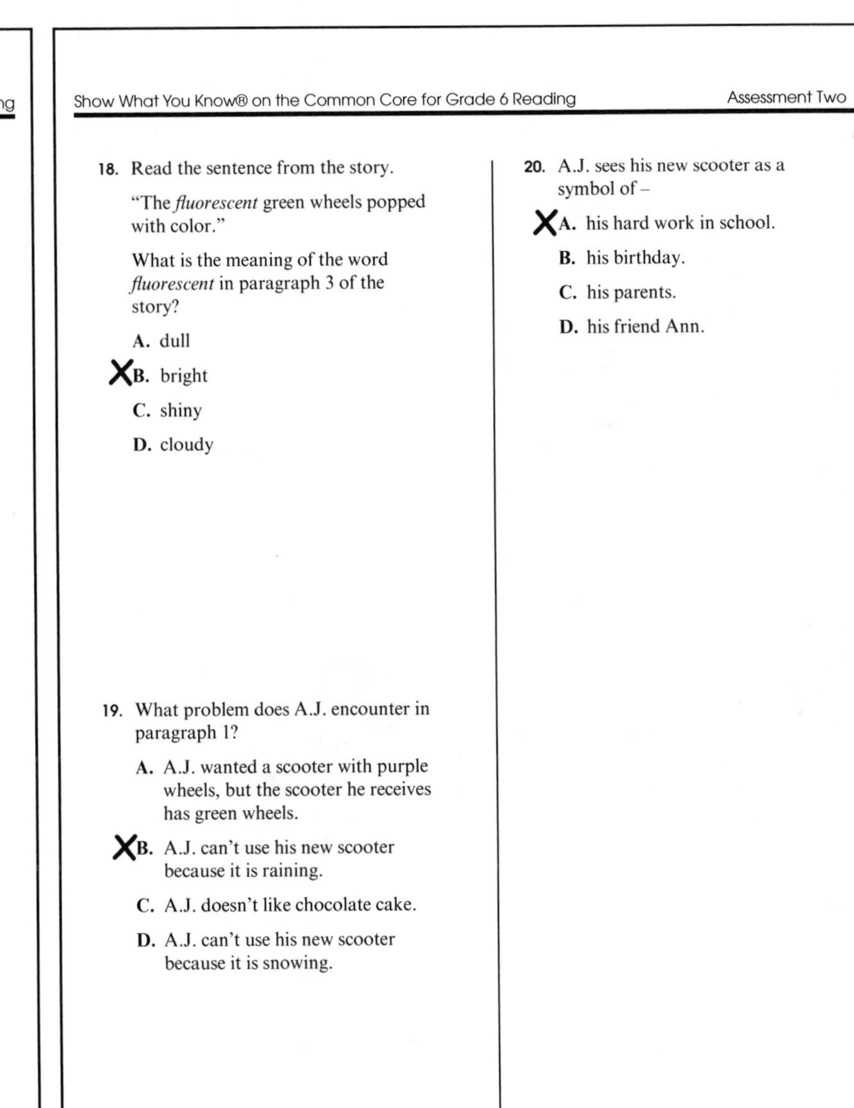

18. Read the sentence from the story.

"The *fluorescent* green wheels popped with color."

What is the meaning of the word *fluorescent* in paragraph 3 of the story?

A. dull

X **B.** bright

C. shiny

D. cloudy

19. What problem does A.J. encounter in paragraph 1?

A. A.J. wanted a scooter with purple wheels, but the scooter he receives has green wheels.

X **B.** A.J. can't use his new scooter because it is raining.

C. A.J. doesn't like chocolate cake.

D. A.J. can't use his new scooter because it is snowing.

20. A.J. sees his new scooter as a symbol of –

X **A.** his hard work in school.

B. his birthday.

C. his parents.

D. his friend Ann.

Go On

Read this selection. Then answer the questions that follow.

A Different Sort of Summer

1 It was the first day of summer vacation after his sixth-grade year, and Javier was thrilled. He couldn't wait for all the things summer would bring: swimming at the local pool, playing baseball in the park, and the chance to play his new video game all the way through. The warm days stretched in front of him with no end in sight. At breakfast on his first day off, however, his dreams of an endless summer were shattered.

2 "Javier," his father said, "starting tomorrow, I want you to come and work with me three or four days every week. It's fine for you to play games and hang out with your friends some of the time, but I don't want you killing off all your brain cells splashing around in the pool or sitting in front of the TV. Some relaxation is fine, but I think you should do something useful with your summer as well."

3 Javier began to protest, but his father declared the matter closed to argument. His father worked at a retirement center. All Javier could think about was how much fun he would miss out on while having to spend time with other people's grandparents. He couldn't even begin to imagine what he would have in common with people so much older than him. He thought about it so much that he didn't even enjoy his first day away from school.

4 At 7:30 sharp the next morning, Javier's alarm began to buzz. With a groan, he rolled over and turned it off. As much as he wanted to go back to sleep, he knew his father would wake him up again in a few minutes anyway. Javier showered, dressed, and went down to join his father.

5 Throughout the entire ride to the retirement center, Javier didn't speak a single word. The car pulled into the parking lot. Javier's father turned off the car, but he didn't open his door. "Javier," he said, "I know this isn't what you wanted to be doing with your summer vacation, but please try to keep an open mind. You may not think any of these people have anything to say that is worth your time, but it's really just the opposite. The longer you are alive, the more interesting experiences you have to talk about." Javier nodded. He didn't believe his father, but he didn't want to pick a fight.

Go On

6 When the two entered the building, Javier's father went to his office to take care of what he called his "silly little morning tasks." Javier wandered around the building, trying to decide what would make the day go the fastest. He settled on a room with a giant TV that was playing an old army movie. He had only been watching for a few moments when someone else entered the room. Javier looked up to see a tall man with silver hair and sharp blue eyes.

7 "Hello, son," the man said to Javier. "My name's William. But call me Big Bill—everyone else around here does." Big Bill looked at the TV screen and laughed. "That doesn't look anything like the army I was in. Those TV guys don't have a clue."

8 Javier could feel his eyes widen. "You were in the army? Wow. I can't even imagine being a soldier. What was it like?" He turned so he could better hear Big Bill's tales of army drills and training camp. The next time Javier looked up at the clock, an hour had passed, and his father was standing in the doorway, watching his son and smiling.

Go On

21. What is most likely the author's purpose for writing "A Different Sort of Summer"?
   - **A.** to describe life in the army to the reader
   - **B.** to persuade the reader to visit retirement centers
   - X **C.** to entertain the reader with a story about a boy learning about other people
   - **D.** to explain the idea of summer vacation

22. How does Javier feel about his dad throughout the majority of the story?
   - **A.** thrilled
   - **B.** disappointed
   - X **C.** upset
   - **D.** interested

23. How does Javier change in the story?

   Support your answer with **two** details from the story.

   Short-answer responses may vary. At first, Javier did not want to go to the retirement center. He tried to protest, but his dad refused to listen to him. When Big Bill starts talking about his life in the army, Javier realizes that being at the retirement center isn't such a bad thing after all. He realizes that he might have more to talk about with some of the residents than he thought he would.

Go On

24. What is the main idea of "A Different Sort of Summer"?
   - **A.** Javier meets an interesting man named Big Bill and enjoys listening to him talk about being in the army.
   - **B.** Javier has an exciting summer planned with his friends, but instead is forced to go to work with his dad.
   - X **C.** Javier reluctantly goes to the retirement center, but realizes that he enjoys listening to the residents talk about their lives.
   - **D.** Javier's dad forces Javier to spend part of the summer going to work with him at the retirement center.

25. Which of the following sentences explains why Javier's father is smiling at the end of the story?
   - X **A.** He is proud of Javier.
   - **B.** He is pleased with himself.
   - **C.** He is enjoying Big Bill's story.
   - **D.** He is done working for the day.

Go On

Read this selection. Then answer the questions that follow.

Our National Bird

1 The bald eagle was chosen as the national symbol of the United States in 1782. It was chosen because of its long life, great strength, and majestic looks. At that time, people also believed that the bald eagle existed only in the area known as the United States. The eagle became a national emblem with the adoption of the Great Seal of the United States. The bald eagle serves as a sign of greatness and represents freedom. You can see the eagle on some U.S. coins, such as the quarter, the silver dollar, and the half dollar.

2 Eagles are large and beautiful birds with long, broad wingspans—from 70–90 inches. This helps them soar high in the air. Adult eagles have blackish-brown feathers on their bodies and white heads, necks, and tails. Some believe the white feathers on the eagle's head give it the appearance of being bald. At one time the word "bald" meant "white." However, the eagle really isn't bald or featherless at all.

3 Eagles are at the top of the food chain and have very few enemies. The eagle's powerful beak can tear through the prey it catches with its strong legs and talons. A part of the sea fish eagle group, these birds will eat both freshwater and saltwater fish. Eagles are known for their excellent eyesight and are able to see fish in the water from several hundred feet above. When they see a fish in the water, they will swoop down and catch it with their sharp talons or claws. Although they are mainly fish eaters, they will also feast on other available food sources, including dead animals. This fact adds to the eagle's reputation as a scavenger.

Go On

4 In the wild, eagles can live to be twenty or thirty years old. They are found in most of North America, ranging from Alaska and Canada to northern Mexico. The bald eagle was put on the endangered species list in 1967 because the birds were dying out. The birds have since made a reappearance, however. Today, there are about 50,000 bald eagles in the United States, and they are no longer considered an endangered species.

The Great Seal

1 The Great Seal of the United States shows a wide-spread bald eagle. On the eagle's breast, a shield appears. The shield contains thirteen parallel red and white stripes. Also present is a blue field with 13 stars. In the eagle's right talon, there is an olive branch. The left talon carries a bundle of thirteen arrows. In the eagle's beak, the bird carries a scroll inscribed with the motto *e pluribus unum*, which translates as "one out of many."

Go On

26. Which of the following is an effect of the bald eagle becoming designated as an endangered species?

A. "In the wild, eagles can live to be twenty or thirty years old."

X B. "Today, there are about 50,000 bald eagles in the United States, and they are no longer considered an endangered species."

C. "Eagles are on the top of the food chain and have very few enemies."

D. "The eagle became a national emblem with the adoption of the Great Seal of the United States."

27. What is most likely the author's purpose for writing this selection?

A. to entertain readers with stories about eagles

X B. to inform readers about the importance of the bald eagle

C. to persuade readers to become involved with endangered species groups

D. to describe to readers what the Great Seal of the United States looks like

Go On

28. Read the sentence from the selection.

"In the eagle's beak, the bird carries a *scroll* inscribed with the motto *e pluribus unum*, which translates as 'one out of many.' "

What is the meaning of the word *scroll* as it is used in the sentence above?

X A. a roll of parchment paper with writing on it

B. an ancient book

C. a list of names

D. to unroll

29. If the bald eagle had not been placed on the Great Seal of the United States, then–

A. the bald eagle probably would not exist outside of the United States.

B. the bald eagle probably would be pictured on all United States coins.

X C. the bald eagle probably would not have become a national emblem.

D. the bald eagle probably would not have a reputation as a scavenger.

Go On

30. Which of the following explains how the bald eagle received its name?

A. The head of the bald eagle is featherless, but the rest of the bird has feathers.

X B. The word "bald" once meant "white," and the bald eagle has white feathers on its head.

C. The bald eagle is a featherless bird.

D. The word "white" once meant "bald," and the bald eagle's head is featherless.

31. Both "Our National Bird" and "The Great Seal" talk about the bald eagle as–

X A. a symbol of the United States.

B. a bird with very few natural enemies.

C. a bird that only exists in the United States.

D. a picture on coins such as quarters and silver dollars.

Go On

32. Which of the following statements is true?

A. The bald eagle eats only freshwater fish.

B. The bald eagle is primarily a scavenger.

C. The bald eagle was close to extinction because it is the prey of many other animals.

X D. The bald eagle hunts by sight.

33. Read the sentence from the selection.

"It was chosen because of its long life, great strength, and *majestic* looks."

Which word could the author have used in paragraph 1 instead of *majestic*?

A. unrefined

B. humble

C. custom

X D. grand

34. Which of the following does not represent a reason why the bald eagle was chosen as a national symbol for the United States?

A. At the time the bird was chosen, people believed the bald eagle could only be found in the United States.

B. The bald eagle has great strength.

X C. The bald eagle is actually bald; at one time, the word "bald" meant "white."

D. The bald eagle has a long life span.

Go On

Read this selection. Then answer the questions that follow.

A Robot Named Dot

1 The nurse came in. The nurse went out. The nurse came in. The nurse went out. That was Elisa's bed-bound, hospital life before a robot named Dot. Elisa was so bored sitting in her bed all day waiting to get well. She missed her friends tremendously. But after Dot came, all of Elisa's burdens disappeared. She could see her friends everyday and actually go to class while she was stuck recovering from the infection in her stomach.

2 While at school one day, Elisa suffered from a horrible stomachache and became very ill. The pain in her stomach was awful! She felt like it would explode if she didn't see the doctor in time! Elisa was immediately sent to the hospital, diagnosed with appendicitis, and had surgery to get her appendix (a small organ attached to the large intestine) removed.

3 After surgery, Elisa still felt very sick. She was exhausted and her stomach still hurt a little. The doctors told her she would have to miss a week or two of school until she felt better. But in the mean time, she would be given Dot, a robot that would allow Elisa to see her friends and go to class while she was lying in her hospital bed. Elisa couldn't believe a robot could do all that!

4 "How could a robot take me to school when I have to stay in this bed all day?" Elisa thought.

5 The following day, the doctor's rolled Dot into her room. Dot was about five feet tall. She looked like a kid covered by an aluminum-can. Dot had a television screen on her stomach and above the screen there was a camera that recorded a picture of Elisa.

6 "Why does the robot need to record a picture of me?" Elisa asked.

7 The doctors explained that Dot had a sister named Dash. They said Dot would stand at Elisa's bedside while the sister robot, Dash, went to school. Dash would send Dot a video of what was happening in Elisa's class and Elisa could watch her teacher and classmates on the television screen on Dot's stomach.

Go On

8 When Elisa had a question, she could make Dash raise its hand so she could ask her teacher. Elisa's teacher could see a picture of Elisa on Dash, and she could hear Elisa's question as if Elisa was in the class with her.

9 Elisa could also use Dot and Dash to communicate with her friends after class. They could see Elisa, and Elisa could see them. It was like they were having a conversation through the television!

10 Elisa couldn't believe it! She was going to get to see her teacher and friends again. She missed going to school very much, but she especially missed her friends. This was what Dot fixed when she came into Elisa's life. Elisa had once been so bored and lonely and now it was almost like she never had to leave school.

11 After Elisa had Dot and Dash to help her, she didn't mind staying in the hospital. Elisa used the robots to go to class everyday. She felt sick some days, but it was always nice for her to know that her friends were just a robot away.

Go On

35. Why does Elisa get the robot named Dot?

A. because she needs tutoring outside of school

B. because she always wanted a robot

X C. because she cannot go to school

D. because she is bored and Dot will entertain her

36. How is the robot Dot different from the robot Dash?

A. Dot has a video screen; Dash only has a speaker.

X B. Dash goes to school; Dot stays in the hospital room.

C. Dot goes to school; Dash stays in the hospital room.

D. Dot and Dash transfer video images between the class and the narrator.

Go On

37. Read the sentence from paragraph 11 of the selection.

"She felt sick some days, but it was always nice for her to know that her friends were *just a robot away*."

What does the author mean by the phrase *just a robot away*?

A. Elisa's friends are just like robots.

B. Elisa's friends are standing just behind her robot.

X C. Elisa's friends are available to her through a robot.

D. Elisa's friends don't like talking through a robot.

38. Which of the following BEST summarizes "A Robot Named Dot"?

A. Elisa goes to the hospital to have her appendix removed.

B. Dot and Dash help Elisa go to school.

C. Elisa uses a robot to talk to her friends and her teacher.

X D. Elisa is bored and lonely in the hospital until robots Dot and Dash come along.

Go On

39. Dot and Dash allow Elisa to do all of the following except—

A. ask her teacher a question.

X**B.** turn in her homework.

C. talk to her classmates.

D. read what is written on the chalkboard.

40. For Elisa, what is the worst part of being in the hospital?

A. being sick and in pain

B. falling behind in her classes

X**C.** loneliness and boredom

D. repeated visits by the nurse

STOP

1 Ⓐ Ⓑ ● Ⓓ

2 ● Ⓑ Ⓒ Ⓓ

3 Ⓐ Ⓑ ● Ⓓ

4 Ⓐ Ⓑ Ⓒ ●

5 Ⓐ ● Ⓒ Ⓓ

6 Ⓐ ● Ⓒ Ⓓ

7

Extended-response answers may vary. The article conveys the depth of the controversy surrounding the construction of a new Megamart by describing the extreme reactions of the citizens following the mayor's announcement. However, the article does not give equal space to both sides in the debate. The article quotes both the mayor and resident Julie Simmons, who list numerous arguments in favor of building the Megamart. The only argument against Megamart is presented by the mayor, who is pro-Megamart. He admits that Megamart has the "reputation for closing small local businesses wherever it goes," but he continues by saying that the benefits of building a new Megamart will outweigh the disadvantages. The article does not quote anyone who is against the new Megamart.

8 Ⓐ Ⓑ ● Ⓓ

9 Ⓐ Ⓑ Ⓒ ●

10 Ⓐ Ⓑ Ⓒ ●

11 Ⓐ ● Ⓒ Ⓓ

12 Ⓐ ● Ⓒ Ⓓ

13

Short-answer responses may vary. I think that Trevor makes a stronger argument about winter because he states more examples of why people should dislike winter than Sheryl's passage states about why people should like winter. Trevor says that most people believe his argument, so that probably means that it is a strong one. I agree with Trevor when he says that the winter is dark and gloomy because it's dark outside more often and everything is cold—too cold.

14 Ⓐ Ⓑ Ⓒ ●

15 ● Ⓑ Ⓒ Ⓓ

16 Ⓐ Ⓑ Ⓒ ●

17 Ⓐ ● Ⓒ Ⓓ

18 Ⓐ ● Ⓒ Ⓓ

19 Ⓐ ● Ⓒ Ⓓ

20 ● Ⓑ Ⓒ Ⓓ

Copying is Prohibited
© Englefield & Associates, Inc.

21 Ⓐ Ⓑ ● Ⓓ

22 Ⓐ Ⓑ ● Ⓓ

23

Short-answer responses may vary. At first, Javier did not want to go to the retirement center. He tried to protest, but his dad refused to listen to him. When Big Bill starts talking about his life in the army, Javier realizes that being at the retirement center isn't such a bad thing after all. He realizes that he might have more to talk about with some of the residents than he thought he would.

24 Ⓐ Ⓑ ● Ⓓ

25 ● Ⓑ Ⓒ Ⓓ

26 Ⓐ ● Ⓒ Ⓓ

27 Ⓐ ● Ⓒ Ⓓ

28 ● Ⓑ Ⓒ Ⓓ

29 Ⓐ Ⓑ ● Ⓓ

30 Ⓐ ● Ⓒ Ⓓ

31 ● Ⓑ Ⓒ Ⓓ

32 Ⓐ Ⓑ Ⓒ ●

33 Ⓐ Ⓑ Ⓒ ●

34 Ⓐ Ⓑ ● Ⓓ

35 Ⓐ Ⓑ ● Ⓓ

36 Ⓐ ● Ⓒ Ⓓ

37 Ⓐ Ⓑ ● Ⓓ

38 Ⓐ Ⓑ Ⓒ ●

39 Ⓐ ● Ⓒ Ⓓ

40 Ⓐ Ⓑ ● Ⓓ

Copying is Prohibited
© Englefield & Associates, Inc.

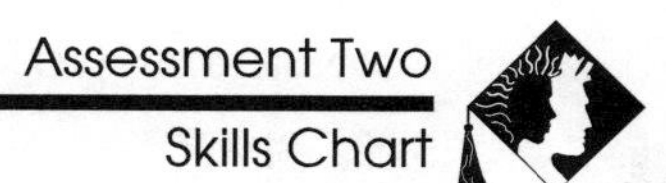

Question	Standard	Answer	Keywords
1	RI.6.6	C	Author's Purpose
2	RI.6.2	A	Cause and Effect
3	RI.6.1	C	Main Idea
4	RI.6.2	D	Summary
5	RI.6.5	B	Differentiate Fact from Opinion in a Variety of Texts
6	RI.6.9	B	Compare and Contrast
7	RI.6.7	—	Main Idea
8	RI.6.8	C	Context Clues
9	RI.6.8	D	Evaluate Arguments
10	RI.6.10	D	Use Text Structure to Locate Information
11	RI.6.4	B	Comprehension
12	RI.6.6	B	Use Text Structure to Locate Information
13	RI.6.8	—	Evaluate Arguments
14	RI.6.4	D	Use Text Structure to Locate Information
15	RI.6.6	A	Author's Purpose
16	RL.6.10	D	Analyze Character Traits
17	RL.6.5	B	Author's Purpose
18	RL.6.4	B	Interpret Vocabulary
19	RL.6.3	B	Analyze Plot
20	RL.6.10	A	Recognize Plot Devices

—see analysis for constructed response

Question	Standard	Answer	Keywords
21	RL.6.10	C	Author's Purpose
22	RL.6.10	C	Analyze Characters
23	RL.6.3	—	Character Development
24	RL.6.2	C	Central Idea
25	RL.6.1	A	Make Connections and Textual Evidence
26	RI.6.1	B	Cause and Effect
27	RI.6.6	B	Author's Purpose
28	RI.6.4	A	Word Definition
29	RI.6.10	C	Connect Ideas Across Text
30	RI.6.1	B	Support Responses Using Text
31	RI.6.9	A	Compare Themes Across Text
32	RI.6.8	D	Fact and Opinion
33	RI.6.5	D	Interpret Vocabulary
34	RI.6.1	C	Support Responses Using Text
35	RL.6.3	C	Cause and Effect
36	RL.6.10	B	Compare and Contrast
37	RL.6.4	C	Define Words
38	RL.6.2	D	Summary
39	RL.6.1	B	Reading to Define Problems
40	RL.6.10	C	Context Clues

—see analysis for constructed response

Copying is Prohibited
© Englefield & Associates, Inc.

Reading Assessment Two: Correlation Chart

Use this chart to identify areas for improvement for individual students or for the class as a whole. For example, enter students' names in the left-hand column. When a student misses a question, place an "X" in the corresponding box. A column with a large number of "Xs" shows that the class needs more practice with that particular objective.

Correlation	RI.6.6	RI.6.2	RI.6.1	RI.6.2	RI.6.5	RI.6.9	RI.6.7	RI.6.8	RI.6.8	RI.6.10	RI.6.4	RI.6.6	RI.6.8	RI.6.4	RI.6.6	RL.6.10	RL.6.5	RL.6.4	RL.6.3	RL.6.10
Answer	C	A	C	D	B	B	—	C	D	D	B	B	—	D	A	D	B	B	B	A
Question	1	2	3	4	5	6	7	8	9	10	11	12	13	14	15	16	17	18	19	20
Student Names																				

—see analysis for constructed response

© Englefield & Associates, Inc.
Copying is Prohibited

Question	21	22	23	24	25	26	27	28	29	30	31	32	33	34	35	36	37	38	39	40
Answer	C	C	—	C	A	B	B	A	C	B	A	D	D	C	C	B	C	D	B	C
Correlation	RL.6.10	RL.6.10	RL.6.3	RL.6.2	RL.6.1	RI.6.1	RI.6.6	RI.6.4	RI.6.10	RI.6.1	RI.6.9	RI.6.8	RI.6.5	RI.6.1	RL.6.3	RL.6.10	RL.6.4	RL.6.2	RL.6.1	RL.6.10

Student Names

—see analysis for constructed response

Copying is Prohibited

© Englefield & Associates, Inc.

For most state proficiency tests, students will answer multiple-choice, short-answer, and extended-response questions.

Multiple-Choice Items: Multiple-choice items have four answer choices, and only one is correct. Multiple-choice items are usually worth one point each. An item with no response will be automatically counted as incorrect.

Short-Answer Items: Short-answer items will require students to write a word, a phrase, or a sentence or two. Student responses receive a score of 0, 1, or 2 points. Each short-answer item has an item-specific scoring guideline. Here is a 2-point short-answer scoring rubric sample:

A **2-point response** provides a complete interpretation and/or correct solution. It demonstrates a thorough understanding of the concept or task. It indicates logical reasoning and conclusions. It is accurate, relevant, and complete.

A **1-point response** provides evidence of a partial interpretation and/or solution process. It demonstrates an incomplete understanding of the concept or task. It contains minor flaws in reasoning. It neglects to address some aspect of the task.

A **Zero-point response** does not meet the criteria required to earn one point. The response indicates inadequate understanding of the task and/or the idea or concept needed to answer the item. It may only repeat information given in the test item. The response may provide an incorrect solution/response and the provided supportive information may be totally irrelevant to the item, or possibly, no other information is shown. The student may have written on a different topic or written, "I don't know."

Extended-Response Items: Extended-response items usually require students to write a complete sentence or a short paragraph. Student responses receive a score of 0, 1, 2, 3, or 4 points. Each item has an item-specific scoring guideline. Here is a 4-point extended-response scoring rubric sample:

A **4-point response** provides essential aspects of a complete interpretation and/or a correct solution. The response thoroughly addresses the points relevant to the concept or task. It provides strong evidence that information, reasoning, and conclusions have a definite logical relationship. It is clearly focused and organized, showing relevance to the concept, task and/or solution process.

A **3-point response** provides essential elements of an interpretation and/or a solution. It addresses the points relevant to the concept or task. It provides ample evidence that information, reasoning, and conclusions have a logical relationship. It is focused and organized, showing relevance to the concept, task, or solution process.

A **2-point response** provides a partial interpretation and/or solution. It somewhat addresses the points relevant to the concept or task. It provides some evidence that information, reasoning, and conclusions have a relationship. It is relevant to the concept and/or task, but there are gaps in focus and organization.

A **1-point response** provides an unclear, inaccurate interpretation and/or solution. It fails to address or omits significant aspects of the concept or task. It provides unrelated or unclear evidence that information, reasoning, and conclusions have a relationship. There is little evidence of focus or organization relevant to the concept, task, and /or solution process.

A **Zero-point response** does not meet the criteria required to earn one point. The response indicates inadequate understanding of the task and/or the idea or concept needed to answer the item. It may only repeat information given in the test item. The response may provide an incorrect solution/response and the provided supportive information may be totally irrelevant to the item, or possibly, no other information is shown. The student may have written on a different topic or written, "I don't know."

Show What You Know® on the COMMON CORE

Assessing Student Knowledge of the Common Core State Standards (CCSS)
Reading • Mathematics • Grades 3–8

Diagnostic Test-Preparation Student Workbooks and Parent/Teacher Editions for Grades 3–5

Single Subject Student Workbooks and Parent/Teacher Editions for Grades 6–8

For more information, call our toll-free number: 1.877.PASSING (727.7464)
or visit our website: www.showwhatyouknowpublishing.com